FALSE RIVER

FALSE RIVER

DOMINIQUE BOTHA

UMUZI

Published in 2013 by Umuzi
an imprint of Random House Struik (Pty) Ltd
Company Reg No 1966/003153/07
First Floor, Wembley Square, Solan Road, Cape Town, 8001, South Africa
PO Box 1144, Cape Town, 8000, South Africa
umuzi@randomstruik.co.za
www.randomstruik.co.za

The photograph of Dominique and Paul Botha on the cover was taken on the
farm Rietpan. The illustration used on the end papers is by John Samuel and
shows the homestead on Thornvale, i.e. Wolwefontein.

The line quoted on page 123 is from the poem "Winternag"
by Eugène Marais.

First edition, first printing 2013

1 3 5 7 9 8 6 4 2

ISBN 978-1-4152-0381-1 (Print)
ISBN 978-1-4152-0540-2 (ePub)
ISBN 978-1-4152-0541-9 (PDF)

Cover design by Michiel Botha
Text design by Monique Cleghorn
Set in Adobe Garamond

Printed and bound in South Africa by CTP Printers, Cape Town

Ook in Afrikaans as *Valsrivier* beskikbaar.

This book is for Andries and Sandra Botha
&
Christiaan, Nadia, André & Adi

As trees are the remembered bones of departed flesh, so the spirit imparts its own epitaph.   – PAUL BOTHA (1970–1997)

CHAPTER I

"You are too close to the water," Paul whispered. "There are barbels in the mud. They will wake up if you step on them."

He pushed past towards the sweet thorn shade.

I saw a dead carp with its eye rotted away. Finches were chattering in the reeds. The water in the pan stank.

"I don't believe you."

"It's true. Barbels aren't like normal fish. They grow as big as men and they eat mud. When it's dark, they crawl up to the house on their shoulders to graze on the lawn."

I ran to catch up with him. "Ma says if you feed silkworms beetroot, they weave threads of crimson. Is that true? I mean, what does crimson mean?"

"It means red. Hurry up you spastic."

I kept silkworms in a shoebox on top of my piano. Ma told me mulberries and silkworms came from China long before our country became the only one in the world. She said silkworms could be tricked into spinning hearts and clovers. If you left them in peace, they spun cocoons the colour of farm butter. At night pale-winged moths fluttered up against the shoebox lid and laid eggs stuck together like crochet beads. Then they died and moth dust silvered the cardboard floor. It was a long walk to the only mulberry tree that grew on our farm. Its roots were lifting the graveyard walls near the ruins of the old house and Pa was threatening to cut the bloody thing down. Ma said he should fix the wall instead.

Paul walked ahead along the footpath that ribboned through the long grass.

Leguaans lived around the pan. That was definitely true. They can whip you off your feet with their tails and they eat snakes, even rinkhalse or pofadders. Abram once killed a leguaan with his pickaxe and brought it to the house. Ma was upset. "He's just going to use it for muti or some nonsense," Pa said. Abram told me leguaans destroyed his fish traps. Even in death the giant lizard held fast to its electric colouring. The long nails at the end of the claws drew lines on the brick paving as Abram dragged it away by the tail.

"Look," Paul said, pointing at some veld lilies sprouting in a groove of cracked mud. "A cluster of midday stars." There were more blooming in the shade of the cemetery wall. I bent down to touch them. Paul went inside and lay down on the grave of our great-grandfather Paul Michiel Botha, which was the family name for firstborn boys. The gate whistled on its hinges like a wire toy made by the piccanins at the stat.

"You shouldn't do that," I said, lingering at the gatepost.

Along the wall grew blue teardrop trees that tolled with singing pigeons. Ma called them graveyard cypresses. "Listen to the birds," Paul said, closing his eyes and putting his feet up. He called them Sunday afternoon doves.

Our family tree had dropped many branches into the graveyard. Lots of Paul Michiel Bothas and their wives and children cut down by the Great Trek, the Great Flu and great age. I walked through the gate, sat down next to the smallest tombstone and trailed my fingers across remnants of chiselled High Dutch effaced by a century of rain.

"What does it say?" I asked.

Petronella Botha. 1880 tot 1887. Hier rust ons geliefde dogtertji, dees aard was niet uw lot.

"I could have been her twin, if I were born a hundred years ago. Dutch sounds like Afrikaans spoken by a person who is mentally retarded." Paul was ten years old and could speak Afrikaans and English. Pa said that made you a true South African.

Oupa- and Oumagrootjie, our great-grandparents, had the fanciest grave, with black and white marble squares. The district surgeon warned that their first child would be their last, so their firstborn daughter was christened Paul Michiel even though she was a girl. Then Oumagrootjie had twelve boys in succession. I knew this because Pa always told visitors who came for lunch. "Courtesy of the many sons," he would say, smoothing his napkin onto the dining room table, "we were granted Rietpan by the Republic of the Orange Free State in 1875.

8

Jan Brand himself signed the title deed. Pity the damn land surveyor's horse was lame. The land could have stretched to the quarry."

Our Oom Paul was Pa's only brother and twenty-one when a friend shot him through the heart. I lined the letters on his grave with seringa berries. *Laat die lieflikheid van God oor hom wees.* Seringa berries made cattle sick and farmers cursed them for being such hardy trees. It was a man called Du Toit who killed Oom Paul. He ended up in the Soutpansberg and became very rich. Ouma and Oupa never forgave him. Ma said what a thing it must have been for that man to live with. Pa kept Oom Paul's wristwatch and pocketknife in a leather trunk in the sunroom. Paul and I peeked inside even though it was marked *Private.* At the bottom of the trunk were letters, diplomas from agricultural college and a list of farm workers with their maize meal allotment and leave days. Lang Piet, Patrys, Boytjie, Kaffertjie. Oom Paul used to be their boss. In the sunroom dead bees piled up below compilations of the *Reader's Digest.* Paul always read the vocabulary quiz and he knew all the words. Sometimes I found dry bats under the wicker chairs.

Paul got up from the gravestone and walked towards me.

He was much taller than me and his hair was dark blond. Pa said Paul and Ma had the pale skin and left hands of the Le Roux Huguenots. I looked up our eye colours in a gem chart Pa found at the co-op in town. Paul was amber or tiger's eye. Pa was lace agate blue that darkened when he became angry. There was no gemstone for my colour. "Undecided blue and your chart is silly," Paul said when I showed him. On his birthday Ouma Celia sent a card saying Paul was the cleverest and most handsome of us all.

"You keep watch while I climb the tree." Paul reached for a mulberry branch.

"You told me the old man is not here any more."

"Don't worry," Paul said, "he is definitely not all here." During harvest Cardow told Ma a mad man had come to live in the reservoir. Cardow was Pa's foreman on Groot Rietpan. He said, "Die man se kop raas, miesies, en hy het nie die dompas." The mad man used to live under a tree on the road between Orkney and Viljoenskroon. Pa called him "Hongersnood", because he was always begging for food. Sometimes I went with Ma when she took him maize meal and oranges. She spoke to him in the Sesotho that she was learning through the post. Hongersnood never came out, but I could see him staring at us. Pa said the problem was Ma was speaking to him in the Sotho of King Moshesh.

Paul disappeared into the leaves. It was hot in the sun. I looked around and walked towards the ruins. The house on Klein Rietpan was built with eighty pounds for a remittance man during the depression. In those days the sandveld was still rotten with slangkop. Livestock died in droves with swollen stomachs full of poisonous leaves. Klein Rietpan was quarantined for bubonic plague when Pa was a boy, so he kept the sisal plantation shorn to deter nesting rats. The remittance man was Pa's great-uncle, Oom George, who tried everyone's patience. Oom George used to sit under a silk umbrella on a harnessed tumbrel until he went bankrupt, throwing teff seed over his shoulder like salt for luck. Oupa Boetie did not buy the land back right away, in case the Irish family by marriage claimed he drove Oom George to ruination.

Pa took roof sheets from our old house to make shedding at Groot Rietpan. In the abandoned orchard small hooves used to point from carcasses above bloodied soil when Ma hung venison from the fig tree to ripen. Acacias had sprouted in the gutted planking of our bedrooms to form a ceiling of yellow pompoms. A fragrant creeper dangled in the air from a broken lintel post.

Queen Bess. I remembered the name. Ma took cuttings from Ouma Koeks's rose garden at Wolwefontein. Ouma Koeks loved roses. She said they only survived in the Free State through sheer force of will. She told me roses came from Persia originally and the English brought them here. Pa always called the English perfidious Albions. Paul said that meant bloody Englishmen. I was sad when I first heard we were moving from Klein Rietpan to Groot Rietpan, but Ma said our new house would be a castle. And it was.

Paul jumped down from the tree with his bag stuffed full of mulberry leaves. He had scratched *Paul Michiel Botha the 6th* onto the flap of the satchel with a ballpoint pen. "Let's go and swim before it rains."

Paul stepped onto the graveyard wall. From up here we could watch the weather change its mind. I knew clouds that brought rain banked in the west, because Pa either cursed or prayed for them to be there. Pa said we had delusions of grandeur calling our vantage point a hill. He said in the absence of mountains, the sky was our landscape. I watched a mole snake slip out from the rock beneath Paul's feet and disappear into the veld. He jumped off.

"I am going to give Hongersnood something."

Two hoopoes circled each other on the path.

"You said he was not here today." All the people inside Hongersnood's head made me scared.

"He's always here, Dom. He is just not all here." Paul tapped his forehead and rolled his eyes. Paul left him some dried apricots, then held out his hand and we ran across the lucerne pasture towards the farm road. "There's Tokolosh coming with the milk tractor. He'll take us home."

We weren't allowed to call Abram "Tokolosh" but the maids in the house did and laughed when he got angry. He was very short and strong and looked after the milk cows. He wore coloured beads under his blue overall and a bracelet made of duiker skin because he was a toordokter. Pa said that was voodoo claptrap. We waited for Abram under the shade of a honey locust. Ma bought the saplings for fifteen cents each from the government nursery in Aliwal North and Abram planted them along the length of the road. They had to be watered daily and many died. In years to come, Ma promised, the trees on either side of the road would meet and fill with nesting doves. In summer the trees were going to roll out a carpet of ruffled seed pods filled with sweet, sticky gum.

"Dumela Ntate," we said to Abram. He stopped and waited for us to climb on. He took an orange packet of Boxer tobacco from his overall and rolled a cigarette out of newspaper. Ntate means father in Sesotho. That's what we had to call all the grownup men on our farm. Pa said it showed respect.

The tractor rattled past the new stat. Pa had built brick-and-mortar houses for his workers. There were even plans for a shaded garage on the side of each house. Ma said the garages were ludicrous, but she refused to move into our new house until Pa finished building the staff houses, garages and all. "Otherwise they will never get finished because there will be some new harebrained scheme."

On the farm workers' graves were see-through domes filled with wreaths. Some had cracked open and the imitation arums had grown pale and brittle. They were also called lords-and-ladies or cuckoopints. I longed to take a lily but I did not want to be a grave robber.

Paul tugged Abram's arm and shouted over the roar of the diesel engine, "We want to swim, please stop." Abram brought the tractor to a halt near a blue gum firebreak next to the house. The midday sun drew the scent of eucalyptus from fraying barks. Water was the bounty of our farm. Rietpan was named after a vast pan that came and went. Lions used to stalk from the bulrushes before the game was driven off. Pa said Rietpan lay at the end of the Voortrekker trail like a sigh of relief, following Allesverloren, Vergenoeg and Bitterfontein. We undressed and Paul dived in. I held my nose against the stink and waded through algae towards the bulrushes. I was pulled under and came up choking on silt.

"You thought I was a leguaan, I know you did."

"I knew it was you. Leguaans live on the other side of the dam and never come here. Pa said so. So there."

I stuck my tongue out at him. "I am going to tell Pa you did that."

An underground spring kept the water close to our house, even in the driest years, when the rest of the pan withdrew underground and up into the sky. Paul swam closer and picked up a feather stuck in the fronds of a bulrush. He held it out to me. "For your collection," he said. It was the colour of red bishop eggs. Paul called it whispering blue. "The colour is so faint, it can't say its name out loud."

"Let's pretend we are crocodiles," I said. "We must only let our eyes stick out. We can watch the bishop birds make their nests." Ma told me that Paul and I used to be vervet monkeys that lived near the vlei. She sent Ou Piet down to the water with a hessian sack to catch us. They cut off our tails and boiled us clean in the vegetable stockpot. Paul said Ma and Pa sex each other and that was how babies came.

On the day Christiaan was born, I hid under the brass bed because of the pot.

"I know what I want from Father Christmas."

Paul smiled at me but said nothing. Flimsy water spiders glided between the rushes on legs as thin as strands of hair.

"I am going to write him a letter and Mamma said she will post it today. It's a secret."

Paul stood up and spun around, trailing his fingers on the surface and then sinking back. Clouds floated on the water, with bulrushes bending through them like spoons.

"Leave the letter on your pillow. Father Christmas lives in our house."

"He does not, he lives where it snows. Do you know what you want for your birthday? You need to tell Ma."

Paul said, "For my birthday, I would like the school to burn down."

He turned away and started swimming back towards the shore.

I longed for my birthday. I was born in the middle of winter and Paul was born in the middle of summer, on New Year's Day. Pa said Ma's cakes were triumphs of the imagination. When Paul turned ten, she made him a chessboard with chocolate pawns and knights. Paul handed me a willow stick to wipe away leeches. In Japan you could pay for leeches to suck your blood and it made me sick to think about it. I picked up my dress and found a nest of goose eggs.

"Paulie, look."

Their shells were covered in small vanilla spots and gunk. "Let's bake mud cakes with these."

"I've already fetched leaves for your silkworms. I'm bored with this now. I'm going upstairs to read."

In our new house there was even a room where Ma could paint. Sometimes we climbed on the roof to collect doves' eggs, although it was forbidden. Pa shot the doves when Ma went in to town. "Their shit clutters up the bloody gutters and just makes more work for me," he said when she protested.

I shifted from one leg to the other. In summer our lawn rolls down to the water's edge, softly sprung like a ballroom floor, Pa said. Paul started walking up towards the house, then slowed down. "I'll go and fetch my book." He sighed again. "By the way, it's not right to take all the eggs from that nest. Fetch some from the coop."

Pa built the chicken coop to Ma's specifications and called it a hoenderhemel. A heaven for chickens. There were covered hatches and a roaming yard full of lucerne and peach trees. Wire mesh was sunk into the ground to protect the chickens from burrowing badgers. Fairies lived in the rotting willow next to the hoenderhemel, but they were always away when I went to look for them. The fairies sometimes came past when I was sleeping and left guinea fowl feathers or porcupine quills next to my bed.

I took six eggs with warm shells and held the hem of my dress to form a basket. I let the tap run to soften the sand. Pa said one must turn the tap carefully otherwise the thread strips and then it's buggered. I picked out thorns and earthworms and kneaded the slimy mixture like Selina did when she was baking bread. "This is the biggest one I've ever made!" I said, standing back. "I'm fetching Ma so she can see." I ran to the house.

"Don't come inside like that, look how dirty your feet are," Selina said, barring me. "Miesies, die kind soek jou." Ma came to the door. She wore a soft cream dress with brown polka dots that she made with fabric bought from the Indians in Klerksdorp across the Vaal. When I opened the bottle of vanilla essence in the pantry, it smelt like her. I was proud of her for being beautiful. Ma's beauty intruded everywhere she went. Into conversations that stopped mid-sentence, into queues that parted, into officials who turned courteous. I heard Pa tell her that.

"Where have you been?" Ma asked. Christiaan sat in his walking ring.

"Come and see what we have made," I said. "It's my best one, Mamma."

Christiaan was a quiet baby. When I was born, I was sweet and smiley. When Paul was born, he cried all the time and terribly. Ma said she fell in love with him the minute she saw him. Before that she preferred cats, and her white Persian Johannes was in all her wedding photographs. I loved looking at those pictures. Johannes shone like a lit candle. I had never seen a cat like that. You only got them in the cities, they were house cats. Ma followed me down to the water's edge with her eyes shielded against the sun because she was blind without contacts. Paul was making an ox out of clay like Abram had shown him.

Ma pointed at the cracked shells.

"Did you use real eggs?"

"Yes, chicken and goose eggs."

"I don't believe this," she said, her voice hardening. "There are people going hungry, but you have thrown food into the mud! Go to the house immediately. I am going to tell your father about this." She turned away and shouted to Selina as she walked towards the house. "Clean these children please. Then bring in the laundry, that storm is on its way." She looked back at us, frowning as she spoke, "Go to your rooms."

Ma always frowned because she was short-sighted. Selina held me firmly against her apron as she hosed the dirt off my legs. I could feel her tub of snuff pressing against my back. Finches were flocking into the pomegranate hedge. Paul pointed at the horizon and said, "Rain shadows." I crept into the kitchen and Paul followed me.

Oil paintings of fruit and flowers hung along the staircase. Ma had copied them from a book called *Treasures from the Rijksmuseum, Amsterdam*. Unsmiling portraits of the dead people from the graveyard hung along the walls of the passage. Some of them climbed out of the picture frames and knocked on my bedroom door at night.

"Fetch the towels, kleinbaas," Selina said to Paul as she turned on the taps. Pa told Selina to call us by our names, but she always called us kleinmies and kleinbaas when we were alone with her. I got into the shallow water. Selina said white people like to waste. We bathed in silence. "The baas is coming home soon. I must make supper," Selina said, wiping my face clean. Paul dressed himself. Selina gave me the white cotton nightdress Ma had made. There were bluebell flower buttons on the cuffs and embroidered roses on the hem.

I went to my room and sat on the brass bed. It was a family heirloom that came from Ma's side of the family. They were Huguenots from France who fled the Papist rabble. That's what Pa called Roman Catholics. The eiderdown was made of paisley silk and stuffed with the feathers of long-gone geese from Ouma's flock at Wolwefontein.

I heard the kitchen door slam. We weren't meant to slam the door, because glass panes could fall out and shatter. Paul came into my room and sat down beside me. "Pa's home," he said. Pa's footsteps thudded up the teak staircase. Pa had been a gymnast at university and always ran up the stairs.

Suddenly Pa stood in the doorway. "What are you waiting for? Dominique, go to the spare room. Paul, go and fetch my belt." His hands were clenched on his hips.

The spare room was for guests and for hidings.

I hurried down the passage. Paul came with the leather belt and put it on the bed. I plaited and unplaited my hair. "I am sorry," I whispered and started crying.

The radio was switched on.

"Pa's listening to the news," Paul said softly.

I heard him opening the window in the sitting room. Ma begged him not to smoke in the house. We listened as he struck a match. Pa said the news was always the same. Imagined terrorists in imaginary countries. Ma and Pa listened to the news every day, even though they said it was all lies. When the sport came on, Pa switched it off.

"Get up, Paul," he said, as he came into the room. He turned Paul by the shoulders to make him face the wall. He hit him first and harder because he was a boy. Four times. I closed my eyes. "Please, Pappa, please stop." I was crying loudly now. Pa grabbed me by the collar. "Be quiet."

I held my hands behind me. The leather strap burnt my fingers three times. I rubbed my hands together and kissed my fingers to release the sting of the belt.

Pa sat down on the bed.

"It is my duty to teach you the difference between right and wrong," he said, pushing his hand through his short, brown hair. Paul looked at the wall and said nothing. Then he wiped his face on his arm. Pa did not hit his workers like other farmers did. Or make the boss boy do it. Only once did he hit Goldberg with his fist because he lost his temper during planting season because of all the stress. Goldberg was one of Pa's boss boys, but we did not use words like that in our family. Pa said Goldberg was his workshop foreman.

Pa took the belt and walked out of the room. Paul lay down on the bed and turned his back to me. The curtains were drawn to keep out the summer sun. They had the same acanthus pattern as the wallpaper. Ma had copied the design onto the cupboard with tracing paper. Then she carefully coloured in the twirling leaf ends with burnt orange. Paul and I had sat on the bed watching as she painted, making it nice for our guests.

It started raining softly. Paul was crying now. In the end he always cried more than me.

CHAPTER 2

"Why are you standing here with the sparrows?" The bottle store owner looked at me and frowned. He had the veneered voice of a smoker, its coating cracking open along the vowels.

"I have come to collect Mrs Botha's order." That's what Ma told me to say.

His shirt was unbuttoned and I could see a naked, ink-blue woman on his chest, her thighs covered by a pendant of Jesus on the cross that hung from a gold chain around his neck. He shouted over his shoulder, "Get Mrs Botha's order and hurry up you bloody lazy bastards." Ma always made us use the entrance reserved for blacks. The room was dark and cool and smelt of leaking watermelons.

"You know, I'm actually a supporter of you people," he said, leaning forward on the till and licking his teeth, his fermenting breath spilling over the counter. I felt shy among all the black men in front of me. Wage day comes early in December. Some of them wore sandals and had grey and furrowed toenails like Cardow's mother, Stompie, who looked after us when Selina went on leave. Stompie only cut her nails when Pa threw away his old razor blades. She fished them out of the dustbin.

"Oh, there you are." Kobus peered over the partition from the *Whites Only* part of the bottle store. Ma had sent Kobus in from the car to help me. He went outside and came back into the *Non-Whites* section to collect the beer on the counter. Kobus and Johnny came from the orphanage in Winburg. They were much older than we were and came to stay during school holidays because their parents had abandoned them. We were awed by the vastness of their misfortune.

"Your mother really loves kaffirs," Kobus said as we walked back to the car. "It's not right for a white girl to go in there." Kobus had red skin and what Paul called spesiale klas hair. It was very yellow and straight like straw. Johnny was much darker-skinned with a thin moustache he shaved twice a day. When Selina first saw them she whispered, "Dis weggooi-boertjies daai."

18

Kobus loaded the crate of bottles into the boot and went and sat in the front again. "That's not fair," I said. Ma looked up from her newspaper and frowned. "Kobus does not get the chance to be in a car as often as you do." Kobus winked at me in the rear-view mirror.

We drove home down Church Street, past Allem Brothers General Store. Old Mister Allem came from Lebanon in 1917 as a tinker and now they provisioned the whole district. Their success was due to Phoenician trading blood. It was said that the Lebanese were so grateful to be declared white by the Nationalists they would vote for them in perpetuity. There were two doctors in Viljoenskroon, Frankel and Goldberg. The town had seven churches but no synagogue. They had to go to Klerksdorp for that. Pa's foreman Goldberg was named after Dr Goldberg because he had delivered him. A doctor was called only if a black woman was dying. Stompie always fetched Ma when someone was giving birth in the stat. Ma said the young women had such beautiful skins stretched over their bellies and they never made a sound. The Dopper church was the oldest building in town in a garden of sand and cypress trees. Doppers believed dancing was a sin and were against singing of hymns and lighting of candles.

Sprinklers watered cut lawns and cement gnomes smiled onto the street. I wished we could have garden gnomes but Ma said it was common. I folded my hair into a knot and sweat crept down my back. I wanted to wear the same dress every day and it made Ma cross. She said I looked like a poor white. A pair of sun beetles climbed over my feet. The car smelled of Kobus, dust and wilting spinach.

I wound down the window and leant into the wind. Telephone wires looped past and a Paradise whydah bird hopscotched across the marshland. In the vlei's bending wake, jaçanas walked on stilts between floating lily pads and moorhens hid in the water grass. In winter dogs chased geese from the bulrushes and farmers took aim at startled birds and called it a shoot.

Ma made a new signpost for Rietpan because our old one had been shot up. At the turn-off a handful of finches sprayed off a wire fence and fluttered into the maize. Ma wrote *Rietpan* in calligraphy and painted a border of sunflowers around the letters. Rust had spread like broken veins through the bullet holes and the old steel plate had to be replaced. "Klomp dronklap geelgatte," Pa had said, examining the damage caused by drunken cowards.

"There's Oupa Bob and Ouma Celia!" I shouted to Ma as we turned onto the farm road. Oupa Bob's real name was Cornelius Janse Petrus Erasmus and he married Ouma Celia when she turned sixteen. Oupa Bob was a welder and they moved across the platteland looking for work when Ma was little. Ma got sandals or a hairbrush for Christmas if she was lucky. She grew up very poor. Ma told Kobus that Oupa could show him how to weld with a blowtorch because a man with an apprenticeship won't go hungry.

"Tannie, why do they have such a nice car?"

"Ouma's salary and years of savings." Kobus wanted to say Mamma and Pappa in the beginning, but Ma said the people at the orphanage had said to watch out for that.

Ouma's maroon car was like a jewel box with mahogany inlay, leather seats and a gleaming jaguar leaping off the nose. It was a bit like their house in Pretoria, which was filled with carpets, Abyssinian cats fired in porcelain, old photographs and painted plates. Milk came in glass bottles delivered to the gate along a path lined with delicious monsters. In the garden was a dovecote spilling gurgling snowy fantails down spiralling steps when Ouma brought out milked bread for them to eat.

Ouma worked in a furniture shop in Braamfontein in a steel-and-glass skyscraper that was a marvel of engineering. They sold desks, bookcases and ashtrays to businesses in the city and then Ouma drove home on the highway and cooked dinner for Oupa at night. A Dutch Bible with velvet binding lay on the entrance hall table. Ouma liked 1 Corinthians 13 verse 12 the most: *For now we see through a glass, darkly; but then face to face: now I know in part; but then shall I know even as also I am known.* It was written in cross-stitch on linen, framed in lace and glass and hung above the sofa. Pa complained their house was so full of things there was nowhere to sit down.

Paul was waiting in the driveway and ran into Oupa's arms. Black hairs grew out of Oupa's waxy nostrils and he always carried a harmonica in his pocket. Ouma stayed in the car, stroking the choker around her neck. She was worried the commotion would upset her dogs. I used to slide under the table during lunch and watch Ouma send food down to Spokie. Ouma had very tiny feet. I could almost fit into her shoes except they had very high heels. Our house was forbidden to animals. A snake killed my puppy and we had swarms of cats that Pa threatened to shoot, but Ma fed them from the kitchen door and they continued to multiply.

Ma knocked on the car window and said to Ouma, "Let's have something to drink." Selina had made yeast beer with fresh ginger and raisins poured into glass jars that were corked and stored in the cool room. The raisins soaked up liquid and sank to the bottom of the jars like contented ticks. Ouma carried her dogs past the birdbath into the entrance hall. Pa called them ridiculous, coddled pompoms. Ouma Celia had a very narrow waist, long dark hair and her skin was smooth, painted and unlined. "It's because she never smiles," Pa said. Ouma was scarred by her parents' divorce. Ma said Ouma's shame was like an antique mothballed scent bottle in her heart, taken out to douse the family on special occasions.

Kobus dragged the heaviest suitcase up the stairs and I carried Ouma's vanity bag that was bigger than Paul's school satchel. She assembled herself every morning with creams, powders and horsehair pewter brushes that she kept in the ostrich-skin vanity case that shut with silver clasps. Kobus waited until I walked past him then pushed me against the wall. He made me feel sick in the same way grown barbels did when they swam up against me in the dam. "I want to punish you for nine months. I'm going to show you how to make a man happy and you are going to thank me for it."

I kicked him in the shins and bit his arm. He caught my wrist and twisted the skin. Paul arrived on the landing with the dog baskets. I pulled my arm away and a box of cigarettes fell out of his pocket. Kobus and Johnny smoked secretly in the spare room and burnt a hole through the silk eiderdown. Ma was furious and ranted loudly about honesty. Nobody owned up.

When I showed Ma the red mark on my arm she said, "Remember how lucky you are, they don't have homes or families." Ma was dressing boiled hams with apricot jam and cloves. She also put cloves in our mouths wrapped in cotton wool and soaked in gin when we had toothache. She held my wrist under the cold tap. "I hope Ouma did not bring presents for Kobus or Johnny." Ma told me if I were mean again she would tell Pa.

Selina brought a tray of coconut-and-apricot jam cookies into the sitting room. They were called Smutsies or Hertzoggies depending on which side of the Afrikaner political divide the baker's sympathies lay. Pa asked for a Smuts cookie. Pa's family were Bloedsappe. Ouma insisted on asking for Hertzoggies. Pa said some Afrikaners forget too easily the debt of gratitude they owe Jan Smuts. Ouma Celia said, "I forget nothing." Ouma kept a copy of Jopie Fourie's letter he wrote before his execution and always spoke about "our people" after some sherries at lunch.

Oupa Bob coughed and smiled. "As a child I hid under the basin in the bathroom when Smuts bombed us." That was Oupa's reason for not liking the Sappe. His family became miners in Vereeniging after the Boer War ruined them. Other than that he was not interested in politics but would support any party that supported the working man. He always picked his teeth clean after meals and then played his harmonica. Oupa knew every tune from "The Blue Danube" waltz to old "Danny Boy". That was Ouma's favourite. Ouma said the Irish had also suffered at the hands of the British. Ouma divided her Hertzoggies between Bennie, Juweel and Spokie.

"Oh for God's sake, don't waste the biscuits on those stoepkakkertjies," Pa said, "now they'll be begging for food constantly."

Ouma smiled. "Don't let them beg, Andries, just feed them."

Oupa got up and stood by the window to look for mocking chats. They eat butterflies and mimic the clapping sound of wings in flight. Oupa tamed wild birds by imitating their calls. Eventually they perched on his shoulder and ate seeds out of his palm. In Pretoria a laughing dove called Bossie lived on his workshop windowsill.

Ma said, "It's time for an afternoon rest. We are giving out presents tonight and then there is church tomorrow."

Pa got up. "Not a moment too soon." He ran up the teak stairs two steps at a time and pulled the bedroom door shut.

Ma looked at Ouma. "That's what gives him the energy of ten men."

Ouma said, "You drift along the relentless flow of instructions like a sleepwalker, my child."

Ma sighed. "It's the price I have to pay for peace."

Ma would not go to church on Christmas Day because she did not believe in God. That was the worst secret I knew. Paul did not care. Everyone belonged to the Dutch Reformed church and all the children went to Sunday school. In really dry years even the farm workers were brought into the whites-only church to pray for rain.

The last time I went to the NG church with Elsabe, the dominee threw a clay pot from the pulpit and shouted, his voice growing louder and louder, "God scattered the races after the iniquities of Babel. Forever separated by the Lord himself like the shards of this broken vessel. Who is man to question His Word?" He sounded like a demented slaughter pig. Then he stared at us and there was not a sound in the church except for doves roosting in the clerestory windows. Elsabe had to write in her Sunday school book that Catholicism was a religion of idolatry and Romish perversion. The dominee shot pigeons off the church roof through the telescopic lens on his gun. I watched him taking aim while I waited in my piano teacher's garden. She lived opposite the church and played the organ there on Sundays. Ma said doves were a symbol of love and peace and it just goes to show.

The dominee came on huisbesoek once and tried to sell uncut diamonds to Ma and Pa. Everyone knew it was a criminal offence for anyone other than the Oppenheimer family to sell those diamonds. The dominee sat in Pa's chair and spoke about black people as "die swakkere broeders". Ma got cross and asked him whether he had a conscience. "What do you mean, mevroutjie?" he asked, pursing his lips.

"If you believe in apartheid you are either criminally ignorant or just plain criminal." The dominee sped off in his Mercedes.

Pa said, "Now you've gone too far, Sandra."

"At least there should be no more itinerant proselytising for God or gemstones," Ma said. She told us it was common practice for dominees to try to make some money on the side, especially when God sent them to poorer communities. Pa's relatives in the Southern Free State piled their bakkies full of maize, slaughtered lambs and bottles of cream to curry favour at the rectory. Pa's Irish grandmother made Oupa half Anglican so Pa also went to the Anglican church. Paul said the best thing about the Anglican church was it only congregated once a month in Viljoenskroon, as the priest had his main parish in Kroonstad.

Upstairs Kobus told us we were going to hell because we did not go to church every Sunday. Johnny nodded, saying nothing but looking quietly devious.

"I'm an agnostic, I don't believe in heaven or hell," Paul said.

Kobus looked angry. "You think you're so clever, don't you? Using big words and speaking English. You're just a laaitie, I'll teach you a flipping lesson."

"What lesson do you think you can teach me? You don't even know how to read." Kobus grabbed Paul by the collar and then Oupa found us on the landing.

I asked if we could rest in his room. He laughed, picked us up and carried us to the spare room. Paul and I lay on the floor under crocheted blankets and Oupa snored so loudly it was impossible to fall asleep. Oupa hardly ever spoke in an angry voice. Only sometimes, like when he told Pa about the fines. The Labour Department came round to check if blacks were doing jobs reserved for whites and then they would penalise him. Oupa's boys were the equal of any white man at handling the welding machines. He was a shooting champion and his silver trophies weighted down the dining-room sideboard at Deur-die-Blare. That was the name of their house in Boot Street. Sometimes he let Paul shoot cans in the quarry near his welding workshop. We giggled at Oupa's big toes peeping through holes in his socks.

In our entrance hall an enormous fir drooped under silver balls and wire angels. Pa and his men chopped down a tree in the veld so big they needed a wagon to load it. We never found a conifer with the perfect shape, like the ones in pictures with candles at the end of the branches on the front covers of German sheet music.

Eventually Ma called us to get ready. Ouma Koeks had arrived from Wolwefontein. She drove herself now that Oupa Boetie had died, with Victoria her cook and the milk tarts in the beige Mercedes with tinted windows. Ouma was so small she needed a cushion to see over the dashboard. When Ouma first came to the district from Fauresmith, in 1934, all the roads were dirt tracks and car wheels were very narrow. One got stuck everywhere, and she had to wear a dustcoat wherever she travelled. Victoria made the best milk tarts in the district and was the tallest and thinnest woman I had ever seen. "Masai blood," Pa said when I asked him.

Ouma Koeks had blonde hair before it turned grey and she wore it in a bun held in place with a dragonfly pin made of diamonds. She had soft, fragrant hands and played piano until arthritis crippled her fingers. Ouma Koeks always wanted to travel but Oupa Boetie preferred to stay home. He had been the chairman of the United Party in Viljoenskoon, but refused to stand for parliament when asked. "He had the good sense to know he would lose," Pa said. Now Ouma Koeks travelled across the district with her cushion and Victoria.

We ate Christmas dinner in the dining room. The oak table was unfolded to its full length with the spare timber leaves slotted in with copper brackets. Pa was at the head of the table where Oupa Boetie would have sat, and made us hold hands while he said grace in Dutch. Ma liked praying even if she did not believe in God. She said the Dutch words were worn smooth through use and dropped into the circle of held hands like stones into a pond.

I thought about Oupa Boetie in heaven. Ma said there was no separation of the races up there if she understood the Bible correctly. Luckily for believers there would not be any sharing of crockery because the dead don't eat. I pushed my vegetables around the patterns on the printed plate. If we did not eat spinach on Christmas, Pa just let us be. Oupa Bob said to Paul, "Sonny boy, now that you are getting so big, do you know what you want to be when you grow up?"

"I want to be a ballet dancer or own a bookshop," Paul said.

Kobus and Johnny sniggered. Paul loved Nadine in my ballet class and always came inside to watch when she danced. Afterwards he went back to the parking lot to play marbles against himself. Our lessons took place in the town hall with plank flooring and a grand piano on the stage protected by a quilted velvet cover. I tried to imagine the lonely steppes of Russia and frozen St Petersburg while I practised the steps of the cat with my mother-of-pearl satin shoes and pink ribbon laces. Then my ballet teacher would stop the cassette and scream at me for having such enormous feet.

Ma stood up and asked Selina and Victoria to bring fruit cake and sherry through to the entrance hall. We sat on the teak staircase and waited for Oupa to hand out the presents. Pa had bought the staircase that used to stand in the entrance hall of a Randlord mansion in Johannesburg. Luckily for us, Broederbond savages were demolishing all the magnificent buildings in Parktown North, so Pa could buy the teak as scrap.

I got a golden-haired doll in a wedding dress with a lace shawl and a posy of paper flowers. Ma cut silk lining from her own wedding dress to make the outfit and stitched shiny beads onto the doll's cape. Ma and Pa also gave me twenty-four coloured pencils to put in my new school case. Oupa made me a box, hand-plated in brass with a hinged lid, that spelt *Pantoffels* in metal buttons down the side. Ouma wrote in her card that she wished me all the best for big school next year.

Pa gave Ma a string of freshwater pearls and she put them around her neck and asked how she looked in her omkooppêrels. Pa needed to bribe Ma because of something we would not understand, like Ouma's suffering at the hands of her parents' divorce. Paul got a Meccano set and lots of books.

We were sent to bed and I hid in the passage under the riempies bench. I whispered to Paul as he walked past, "Father Christmas is going to climb down the chimney and I want to see him. Come and hide here with me."

Paul just laughed.

The house grew quiet as Pa locked up. I listened out for noises in the chimney. There was vague drumming from the stat. Sounds of the pan tiptoed up the lawn. Frogs, swooping owls, bats, blacksmith plovers, fluttering moths, a faraway jackal calling. I could not hear barbels crawling up on their shoulders. I wanted to ask Pa about that because I was not sure I believed Paul. Ma said you had to put barbels in a vat of clean water for a few days before you could cook them. I thought about their long whiskers, their smooth skins and their big skulls, swimming around and around in circles cleansing their horrible flesh. In the years when the pan dries up, all that remains are shoals of carp and barbels flailing in mud. People pour out of the location to fill up hessian sacks. During the last drought a smell of fish oil hung in the air. The butcher in town complained to Pa that the blacks were not buying red meat.

I heard footsteps. My heart pounded against the frame of the bench. It was not Father Christmas. It was Kobus. The riempies bench stood between my room and Paul's room. I could see Kobus in the dark open my door without even knocking. Then he went into Paul's room, even though Kobus and Johnny were supposed to sleep in the art room, where Ma had beds made for them.

CHAPTER 3

I stood with my face pressed up against the cold glass panes of my bedroom window. The moon cast a bright, silver path across the pan. Faraway stars squinted, then winked. Smoke from a very old fire drifted across the night sky. Roman times were so dark stars spilt over evenings like milk. That's why they called it Via Lactea, Pa said. He liked to quote his school Latin.

I lay down again. Crickets chirped and warbled all night behind skirting boards and in marigold beds. They stridulate by drawing serrated hind legs across shuttered flanks. That was what it said in the *Encyclopaedia Britannica*. We only had the A and the C given for free on trial by a man who drove around the district with a car boot full of books. You could order the rest of the alphabet from England. Ma was going to think about it. Oupa Boetie had books at Wolwefontein that listed livestock diseases alphabetically with illustrations. Ma once bought scabby sheep out of the Karoo. All auctioneers are crooks. The sheep died one by one from mange after their fleece came off in stumps. Pa doesn't like sheep because their grazing wrecks the veld. There was also a book with a woman's body that folded open along an arrowed pleat. Her insides pulled out on a fragile scaffold laced together by paper arteries. Inside a creased womb was a baby fast asleep on a shivering folded hinge.

I could not fall asleep.

Buckled shoes and a green dress lay folded at the foot of my bed. I was lucky. When Pa grew up, bywoners travelled on donkey carts between farms with no money for uniforms. The shop owner had fat hands and complained it was not really worth his while to stock school clothes for so few children. Ma said if schools in the location had the same uniform then he would have a bigger offset. He patted his lips slowly with his chubby fingers. Ma said afterwards she did not like a man with a lush mouth.

I got out of bed and opened the curtain to let moonlight into the hall. At night our passage turned to water and barbels swam below the wood grain. I crept along the wall to Paul's room and shut my eyes against the antlered shadows while the staircase in the entrance hall snapped and groaned.

"Are you sleeping?"I whispered.

Paul didn't mind being woken up, not like Pa on a Sunday afternoon when he threatened and begged us before having an afternoon sleep, "For Christ's sake all I demand is the deference accorded the dead." I sat down on the end of Paul's bed. Brass bobbins wobbled and spun as he shifted around.

"What do you want?"

"I am going to have the same teacher you had."

Paul had a poster of a sprinter stuck above his bed and a book of stamps in his drawer. The sign on the drawer said *Open on Pain of Death*. "That's right. Now good night."

"Why did you not like her?"

"Who said I didn't like her?"

I overheard Ma and Pa talking about Paul and me and a different kettle of fish. I was under their bed playing hide-and-seek with Christiaan, and I could see Pa's khaki boots as he stood next to the window looking out at the pan. His teaspoon went clink-clink against the china cup as he stirred his precisely measured one-and-a-quarter spoons of sugar into his tea.

"Why are you going to the English medium then?" I asked, smoothing my doll's disobedient hair. I named her Sarie Marais. She was my favourite. When little girls came from the stat to play, I made them abba my dolls on their backs. I was the madam and they were the maids.

Paul smiled, "Don't worry, your teacher will like you because you are such a goody two-shoes. You will like your teacher. You like everybody."

"I don't like Kobus. And I don't like the devil."

He groaned and put a pillow over his head, like Pa did when he wanted to sleep.

"You were christened Sliminique, but when they figured out how dim you were they renamed you Dominique." That was better than being called perdebek because of my big teeth.

"At least my middle name is not Michiel." Michiel was the name of the retard at school. It was a very embarrassing name to have. Paul grabbed Sarie Marais by the hair and her head came clean off. I started crying to make Paul scared of Ma and Pa. Paul took the doll's body and clicked her head back on.

"Shhhh, Ma and Pa will wake up. I'm sorry. Please don't cry. Please let me sleep."

I walked out of his room and closed the door slowly. Paul had typed his name on a piece of paper and stuck it on his door at the beginning of the year.

Paul Botha's room. No intruders pleasezzzz. tikka tik tik?!? Zzzzzz beeeeeb BOOM CRASH SPLATTER CRASH*??? Sorry for the slight disturbance. Will my Chainword* CHICKS *please bring me another typewriter.*

He had left out *Michiel.*

Ouma Koeks gave the Olivetti to Paul. It had belonged to Oupa Boetie and before he died he typed letters to his family in the Southern Free State and to the newspapers in high Dutch. Paul said it doesn't matter what your handwriting looks like, it's what you think that counts. Paul's handwriting left much to be desired. That was in his school report, underlined twice in red pen with an exclamation mark by his teacher.

I went back to bed. Just after New Year I fell onto a brass pot and my front tooth died. I was embarrassed to go to school for the first time with a green tooth. Ma said not to worry because it was just a milk tooth that would fall out when its time came. She wove laddered stockings into my wet hair to make curls and lacquered the plaits with spray to make them set, so that no-one would notice the tooth. I fell asleep holding my nose against the dense smell of tadpoles growing in the plastic sunflower oil jar under my bed.

The next morning Ma took a picture of Pa and me standing hand in hand next to the water reservoir: Pa wearing khakis and me, with my tightly sprung ringlets, looking into the January sunrise. In my school case was the pencil bag I got for Christmas and homemade bread smeared with farm butter and fig jam from our orchard. I did not smile because of my green tooth.

Ma drove Paul and me to school in the station wagon and Stompie got a lift to go and see Dr Goldberg about her swollen feet. Black people's blood pressure rose when they grew old but luckily their backs never gave in like whites'. Stompie wheezed a lot because of snorting snuff. She was very strict and would not let us climb trees. She always shouted, "You're going to break!" and then we laughed at her broken sentences and climbed higher up the pepper tree that flourished next to the leaking garden tap at Wolwefontein. When Ouma Celia visited from Pretoria, Stompie would walk all the way from the stat on in-flamed soles to pay respects. They would sit outside on garden chairs while Stompie took snuff from a little blue tub and Ouma drew pencil sketches of the willow trees. They talked about arthritis and crocheting.

Cardow was Stompie's oldest surviving son. The Lekghetas came to us many years ago during the time of reckoning. That was what Ma called August, the month when what was owed and borrowed was tallied and people left farms with their measly belongings to look for work elsewhere. The men's families travelled with them. Cardow came at night on the 3rd of September 1974 and asked for a job and Pa said no. He showed me the date that he first came to Rietpan on a piece of paper he kept in his passbook. The men who wanted work waited for hours and hours behind the workshop outside Pa's line of sight. Cardow came again the next morning and the morning after until Pa relented. Pa says that if it was not for that man, he would not be farming today.

We drove past the Mahem Hotel and Ladies' Bar. Ma said it should be renamed the Mayhem Hotel because of what goes on in there and Paul laughed. Stompie snorted and dark liquid bled from her nostril. A Mahem is a rare crane with a scarlet throat, powdered cheeks and a spiky crown. It was our town emblem. Mahems used to forage in the vlei looking like ladies with lace headdresses stooping for dropped handkerchiefs. We never saw them anymore because farm workers weren't the only ones being poisoned when crop sprayers flew over the fields in spring. When Ma said that, Pa got very cross.

The school stretched the length of Viljoen Street along an avenue of dusty needled Casuarinas. I took Ma's hand and clung to her as we walked to Paul's new class. There were only eleven children in the English medium across three grades. Mrs Pearce had short hair and glasses and taught them simultaneously. For singing, they joined the Afrikaans classes to learn *Die Stem*. There was also a special class for retards. Michiel was the oldest boy in the special class and Paul said they kept to themselves during break.

I waited outside and watched through the window.

Mrs Pearce's top lip protruded slightly. "I am sure his English is adequate, Mrs Botha. With application and discipline he will soon flourish." She turned towards the children crowding around a cardboard box punctured with holes. Paul had told me about the manager's son on Makvoël who caught chameleons and starved them down to the colour of a dry twig. Then he brought them to school to show off. He also told Paul that he and his brothers were waiting for their little sister to ripen like a cherry. Paul went to sit at a desk and took a book out of his suitcase.

"Reading, are we, Paul? Don't you want to see Matthew's rabbits?"

"No thank you, I just want to finish my book before class starts."

"No thank you who?"

"No thank you, Mrs Pearce."

Mrs Pearce had two front teeth that stood at an angle to each other. The tooth that was trying to hide was discoloured. I remembered not to smile. Paul gave a small wave and turned back to his book. Ma took my hand and we walked past a clump of blue gums that grew in a courtyard of gravel. Sprinklers stroked rooting grass on a rugby field. Bicycles stood under a shading lean-to.

"Who is this?" My teacher bent down, took my hand and smiled. She said I had a beautiful name. Her name was Juffrou. She wore a yellow skirt that hung in pleats below her knees. Her toenails were painted pink and a slender gold chain hung around her neck. Ma said what a woeful collection of haasbekkies.

No need arose for soft and serious conversations between Juffrou and Ma. Juffrou's chalkboard hieroglyphs revealed their secrets. Words and sentences followed. Numbers made sense. I found a friend. My report card said *Diligent, obedient and neat.* Ma and Pa were proud. Juffrou was pleased. She called me Dominique, not Nonsense like they did at home, because at school I spoke less.

Ma decided Paul should learn to play an instrument. Our music teacher Mrs van der Westhuizen had moved to the platteland from the city to marry Mr van der Westhuizen who owned the chemist. Her Steinway was covered in used teacups placed on the headmaster's news-letters to prevent ring stains, and she policed straying fingers with the thin end of a wooden ruler. Mrs van der Westhuizen had two Persian cats called Mattewis and Meraai who smelled of mothballs. During lessons she would clasp sheet music to her chest with closed eyes and say, "Imagine the pastel houses of Prague, imagine Mozart looking out across cobbled streets, through lime trees, across the Vltava towards the mirrored castle." Or, "Mattewis does not like your attack, be more delicate."

Paul said she looked like an ominous spider during theory of music group class on Wednesday afternoons, when she sat at the front and he sat at the back and wrote *kakhuis kakhuis kak* on the middle c line of his notebook. You had to walk up to her desk and submit your com-pleted work for scrutiny. Untidy notes were decried as swatted flies and dismissed with, "Weg met die vlieëmis!" Her students always won first prizes at the Kroonstad Eisteddfod.

Paul hated practising scales. He drew note names in capitals onto the ivory keys of our piano with a ballpoint pen. CDEFGAB. Ma was furious. The ivories looked like dirty fingernails. "Net gekke en dwase skryf op mure en glase!" she shouted. She let him give up though. Then he became a Voortrekker. They learnt skills that were useful during the Boer War. On Fridays they hoisted the National Flag at the parade ground and stood to attention in the sun in brown polyester shorts, long-sleeved shirts and an orange tie pinned down with medals. After one term he refused. He told me that Voortrekker means wanker in English.

Every April an agricultural fair was held at the showground. April is the most beautiful month on the Highveld. Clouds fill the sky mostly for show. Sunflowers nod off. Cosmos peeps through rooigras. The sun discards its sting and pours honey across the late afternoon.

Pa said a town without a fair was not worthy of being called a town. The exhibition hall was a big corrugated iron shed with a concrete floor filled with pumpkins, flower arrangements and the smell of fresh batter and cinnamon. Outside there were goats defecating in small pens, fat sheep bleating and bunting strung along metal poles grown hot in the sun. On the sandy track kapkarre and sierperde pranced while Oom Voëltjie Bezuidenhout announced the winners. Pa never had animals in the show ring. He said it was sad to see grown men compete for pleated silk rosettes. Ma said it was because Pa had no feel for livestock.

For many years the church prevented the show dance on the Friday evening because they were worried about moral decay. Pa gave us pocket money to buy tickets for the fairground swings. We were flung in circles above the black children crowding outside the fence and they waved and smiled. I felt sick from too much spookasem and I closed my eyes. Pa said the irony is those contraptions were death traps and no-one should be allowed on them. Paul said he bet I did not know what irony meant, but I did. It meant something made of iron, like those death traps.

Paul had made a wagon in woodwork class pulled by a team of twelve dolosse that won first prize. Tokolosh was a master at making clay figurines and helped Paul mine clay from the bank below the willows. He broke off the tips of devil's thorns for the horns and used matchsticks to make the yokes. The judges awarded cardboard squares in different colours as prizes for first, second, third and highly commended. One of the judges told Ma that Paul was probably always behind in his schoolwork because his thoughts were so far ahead. I liked the flower arrangements. Only a few blossoms at stiff angles to each other tied with raffia bows to wooden stems. They looked like the wreaths on the farm worker graves at Groot Rietpan.

Sumari Botha came up and stood next to us. She was eating a red toffee apple that cost five cents at the Rotarian stall and had dark curls and a skin like fudge. She was in my class. I asked Pa at the beginning of the year if we were related but he said, "We're not family of those Bothas." Ma said Pa was talking nonsense. She said the Botha family tree was shaped like a conifer, all the branches grew within reach of each other. Sumari bit into the apple and said, "A kaffir hung himself from one of the trees on the parade ground. Isn't it wonderful? Now there is one fewer of them."

During break I sat under the Casuarina trees with Elsabe, eating home-made brown bread. I envied the town children their white sandwiches with polony and margarine. I went looking for Paul at first. Some-times I found the boys in Paul's class playing touches near the school hall where I practised "Für Elise" for the Eisteddfod. The boys in the English medium were called Matthew, Mark, Luke and John. They did not play with boneheads and pulled faces at me. When I found Paul in class, Mrs Pearce lowered her head and looked at me crossly over her glasses. "Paul has to stay in for break because he hasn't finished his work yet." He wrote very slowly and with his left hand. His letters would not stay between the lines.

When Cardow fetched us in the bakkie, I would sink low behind the dashboard to hide. At school they asked, "Sis! How can you sit next to a kaffir like that?" Ma could not always collect us because she was busy arranging to build a farm school. She explained that the govern-ment would reimburse Pa if they expedited the process. Waaisand Primary was built with proper pit latrines and a sign painted in cursive lettering inside a border of twirling leaves. The school also got a red stoep and a red roof because we had paint left over from building the house at Groot Rietpan. Mrs Wilson was helping Ma. She sat in the office at Pa's workshop and phoned around for the best price on bricks and blackboards. She called it procurements. Pa called it prevarications.

Mr Wilson was the wife of Mr Wilson and the mother of Eileen and Mary. The Wilsons were Irish. They had alabaster skin covered in red freckles and spoke singsong English. They rented the house on Aandson that bordered Groot Rietpan and belonged to Pa's cousin Tannie Kotie. Pa had to rent the land from her at usurious rates. Some-times he said, "You must never do anybody a favour, because they will never forgive you." Tannie Kotie lived in Durban and never came to the farm any more and her sons could not even speak Afrikaans.

The Wilsons were the only people from overseas that we had ever met. Paul held Eileen's hand behind the dam. Mary also liked him. Mrs Wilson called Paul a charmer. Pa called Mr Wilson a boozer. One morning Mrs Wilson came to the house in tears because her husband's boss had said it was time to move on. Pa said you can't fit and turn on the bottle.

Paul wanted to give Eileen his stamp collection before they left. He said it would be an adventure. Ma and Pa went to bed and then we climbed through Paul's window and walked along the wenakkers under the moon, past the rubbish dump and the farm workers' graves near the old stat. All the people had moved from the old mud houses except for Fezile. Pa said he was unconscionably obstinate. In the dark his house stood like a live animal amidst crumbling humps of daub and dung. I was worried about the tokolosh and Fezile's pink sow with black ears that grunted at us from a collapsing ogiesdraad cage. We took the drif across the vlei, otherwise we would sink into the churning rot of mud and our feet would stink. I looked back at our beacon. Our farm had the highest contour in the district, even though it was too low to call it a hill. The rise in altitude merited a white cement column with an iron flag painted black as a sentinel to cartographers and land surveyors. We were proud of that. When we got to Aandson, my feet were rubbed to blisters. Mr Wilson screamed about bloody godforsaken irresponsibleness and phoned Pa who fetched us in the bakkie and gave us a hiding when we got home. Paul never gave Eileen the stamps.

When Pa finished building Waaisand Primary a man called Abel Dlamini came to apply for the post of headmaster. That is how it worked, the farmer decided if the applicant was suitable. He knocked on the back door and waited next to the aluminum bowls full of pap and maas for the cats.

Pa invited him into the kitchen and Abel held out his cv in a worn plastic envelope and said, "Dankie Baas." Pa looked up at Abel and said, "Don't call me Baas, I am not the one paying your salary."

Abel said, on the strength of that statement, he went to fetch his wife Mary and they moved into the house next to Waaisand Primary. Abel and Mary Dlamini even had a car and used the garage. Pa liked to point that out to Ma. They also had a teenage daughter called Maureen and a son Vusi who was born the same year as Paul. Mary Dlamini wore suits like Ouma Koeks and called Ma Sandy. She planted a row of cypress trees in her garden and Ma started a gardening competition for the best yard in the stat. Tokolosh won because his sullen children had to plant and water every weekend, away from temptation. He wanted his son to become a priest. He even coaxed camellias to flower in winter and in summer Afrikanertjies lined the herringbone path up to his battered door.

Abel and Mary started adult literacy classes at night. Many farmers allowed people to come on wagons after tjaila time to learn. The two schoolrooms were packed at night with old women wrapped in blankets and old men in suits. When lightning tripped the electricity, Abel would teach the ABC by candlelight. Cardow wanted to get a Standard Five so that he could go to Boskop. That's where farm workers were sent for skills. Maybe even a matric one day, he said. Pa said you had to admire people who had the determination to study after work. He liked to come home and have a whiskey in front of the news, even though it always irritated him.

On the last day of term I was walking back to class from the toilets when I heard our headmaster Mr Kruger screaming at somebody in the quad. On Mondays and Fridays Mr Kruger stood on stage in the assembly hall when we sang the National Anthem, standing to attention, and I was too scared to even look at him. "Live out the school motto," he shouted out in every assembly, "Labor corona vitae. Work is the crown of life."

I peeked from behind a column and saw Mr Kruger pulling Paul by the neck and dragging him along sharp gravel. A gust of wind blew open the music room door and Paul grabbed onto the handle, refusing to move. I turned around and started walking back to class as quickly as was allowed. Running on the walkways was forbidden. I had forgotten to take off my yellow pajama underpants. Juffrou said we would get into trouble if we did not wear the compulsory green Crimplene underwear. When I got back to class, Juffrou asked if I had seen a ghost. I tried to finish colouring in the shapes we were learning in class. Circles, spheres, rectangles and cubes. When the school bell rang I ran out of class into Ma's arms.

"Paul was very bad today," I blurted out. Ma looked stricken.

Paul came out of his class and collapsed against her legs in tears. There was a bandage on his arm. Mrs Pearce said, "Paul just takes his time and expects all of us to wait around. I had to call in Mr Kruger to talk to him. He refused to go to his office. Can you imagine? Then the unfortunate incident. It doesn't do the reputation of the English medium any good."

Paul was writing too slowly and not between the lines. What could she do, she had to call the headmaster. They had had enough of this problem. We stumbled to the car. Paul sat in the front seat and was crying softly with his head in his arms. Ma asked him what happened. "Teacher said she would make sure I failed the year." Ma kept her eyes on the road. When we got back to the farm, Paul ran upstairs to his room and locked the door.

Pa sighed. "In my day, our master hit us with a whip. That old sadist Heron Botha." That was his nickname because he lived next to the vlei where goliath herons preyed on frogs. I remembered Pa telling us about the whip. Everyone was scared of Reier Botha, even Oupa Boetie, because he had more education than anyone in the district.

Ma said nothing. Pa sat with his hands in his hair.

Later that afternoon James and Matthew Henderson rode across on horses along the wenakkers to fish in our pan. "I don't want to see those troglodytes," Paul said. Ma said he was showing off and made him come down to the kitchen. Only our friends were allowed to fish in our dam because the Hengelklub made such a mess on weekends that Pa had to put a stop to it. I followed the boys to the dam. They cast their lines under the willow trees where snakebirds had whitened the branches with excrement.

James wanted to see the wound on Paul's arm so he unravelled the bandage. The school nurse had sewn up the jagged cut and cleaned the wound with Mercurochrome. We were impressed.

James said, "Holy crap." James was able to piss further than anyone else. He impaled an earthworm onto a hook. "Jeez Paul, you're such a retard. You can't even write."

"If you don't want to listen, then you must feel," Matthew said. "You have to respect authority."

I knew that if you did not respect authority they could lock you into the dark cell behind the police station with one small window and a thick iron bar. Sometimes people came to Ma and Pa and complained that the police pulled bags over their heads and beat them in that dark cell if they weren't carrying a pass.

Paul threw a pebble that skimmed the glassy surface of the pan three times, then sank.

"Hey, you're disturbing the fish. What are you doing?" James asked.

"Casting pearls," Paul smiled.

CHAPTER 4

Dinner was the last of the wors from the previous winter's slaughtering. It had been defrosting in a tin on top of the fridge all day and by evening wallowed in a bloody pool covered in plastic and masking tape. Pa decanted the blood into a pan to fry up and eat with salt. I fished out coriander balls when Pa was not looking and asked for sauce. Paul burst out laughing, "It's gravy, you idiot." Pa made a rule that we had to speak English at mealtimes to learn.

Ma was going to take us to see a specialist in the morning. After the unfortunate incident with Paul, Ma went to Dr Frankel who recommended a doctor in Johannesburg. Pa called Johannesburg Sodom and Gomorrah. The specialist could measure your potential and predict your profession. I had been making paper fortune tellers at school during break, writing, behind the folded triangles, what you could be one day. I wanted to be a pianist, but that was impossible. Ma said to be a real musician you needed to be an Ashkenazi Jew from Russia where talent travelled down generations along a golden filament that was lit, once a century or so, by genius. It was impossible to ask about the special doctor in English.

We left early the next morning after pap with milk still warm from the udder. Pa ate two eggs, two pieces of bacon and a slice of toast buttressed by a knife if the silver toast rack was up for polishing. He liked his breakfast to be exactly the same every morning. Pa swallowed his coffee and said, "Nou toe, be on your way now." He chased away the cats on the doormat, begging God to rid him of this feline pestilence.

Winter comes to the Free State at night. In the morning sheets of ice crackle underfoot and leaves are hemmed with frost. Snakes disappear. Rains stay away. The whole world becomes a tinderbox.

I sat in the back of the station wagon with Christiaan. Paul sat in the front with Ma. She switched the radio on. Gum avenues swung past. Cattle egrets stood in the detritus of harvested fields. A long, grey pencil stripe of road ran ahead into the blue hills on the horizon. Ma listened to the news and the weather report. Paul said that the prevailing conditions in all those faraway places made him long to see them.

Ma said, "When I was young I also longed to see faraway places."

The first time Ma saw the sea she was standing on the pier at Cape Town harbour yearning to be on one of the leaving boats. Ouma Celia had taken out a life insurance policy when Ma was born to afford university fees. She went from the waterfront to Stellenbosch to get a degree.

"Now I am back here! In the Free State. Everything ends where it begins, they say." She laughed.

"Do you still want to get away?" Paul asked.

"Yes."

Paul looked up at her. She ruffled her fingers through his hair and smiled.

"I have a busy and fulfilling life here. Especially now that I am handling the cattle farming." Ma took over after Oupa Boetie's death because Pa was not interested in livestock. Paul undid the raffia string on the orange bag at his feet and passed a naartjie to Ma. It made Pa apoplectic if anyone ate in the car.

"Oupa imported Sussex and Herefords from England to crossbreed with our Afrikaner herd. It always amazes me just how far they have travelled. From the English countryside all the way to the Free State by train, by boat and by truck. Thirteen years later the False River broke the hundred-year flood line and the water carried them all away."

Ma wiped her glasses clean with the edge of her blouse.

"Did any survive the flood?" Paul asked.

"We got back every single one."

She wound the window down and threw the naartjie peel out.

"The worst part is when the calves are loaded onto wagons to go to the abattoir. They are always so excited to be going somewhere new. They caper and frolic."

"Why do you do it?" Paul asked.

"I am quite good at it, to my surprise. I work scientifically because I don't know how else."

"How do you know which are the better cattle? How can you tell?" Paul asked.

"You can select them according to colour or how well they walk the veld without their hooves giving trouble. In England the cattle just stand and eat, so that is not important, but obviously here at home they have to walk far for their food."

Mine dumps appeared on the horizon, intimating the city.

"I've never liked Herefords," Ma said. "The white skin around their eyes always gives trouble because of the sun. For many generations the white skips through and shows. I sell everything that has even one white spot."

We drove into the city beneath a highway. I worried the road above might fall on top of us in case of an earthquake like the one in Carletonville, where people's houses disappeared into sinkholes over lunch hour. Ma said the road had been properly engineered. My other nickname was Kommerkous because I worried about silly things. Christiaan was called Renoster Voster because he was gruff. Paul was called Zoontjie. Pa's workers called him Oorlog, but not to his face.

Pa had outlined the route with a red pen and Paul navigated so Ma would not get lost. The doctor's rooms looked like the house on Wolwefontein. In the garden were enormous trees that branched like the respiratory tree diagram in Dr Frankel's consulting rooms. Ma said they were jacaranda trunks full of lilac flowers that would trumpet into bloom in spring. The receptionist smiled at me and asked whether we had French family. I looked at Paul. He said Ma just liked the name Dominique. His name, he explained in English, was the name of all firstborn sons. Paul saw the doctor first. Ma took Christiaan and me to the café next door. I blew bubbles into my fruit juice and laughed so much it went up my nose and I coughed all over Ma's ham-and-cheese sandwich and she was cross.

Afterwards I sat across from Dr Cohen at her desk. She had dark hair and a swollen beauty spot above her top lip. (Ma also had a beauty spot, but it looked pretty on her face. Pa said Ma was more beautiful than Sophia Loren.) Jewish people are cleverer than anybody else. Dr Cohen kept rearranging her glasses with both hands and spoke

Afrikaans with a funny accent. She knew all the words and the right places to put them, just not how to say them. She made me identify circles and squares, do sums and explain feelings on drawn faces.

"Are you happy at home?" she asked.

"Our farm is the best place in the world." She smiled at me.

"Dominique, what we speak about here today will stay between me and you. That is a promise, okay?"

I sat on my hands and looked out the window. A gecko clung to the windowsill. I felt shy. "If you had three wishes, and you could wish for anything at all in the whole world, what would those wishes be?"

I wished that Ma and Pa would vote for the National Party and go to the Dutch Reformed church. I wished we could be the same as everybody else. I knew Paul did not wish that. I also thought of real pointe ballet shoes, finding the willow fairies and playing the violin.

"I would like peace in the world. I would like nobody to starve," I said.

"I see." She frowned. "What is your third wish?"

"To play the violin," I admitted. She seemed happy that I had made a selfish wish.

When she waved us goodbye she promised to be in contact. Paul got to sit in the front again, which was unfair. Christiaan fell asleep. I woke up in the honey locust avenue under the almost-touching fingertips of leafless winter trees. Pa was waiting in the driveway. Blacksmith plovers squeaked and fluted in the long grass. He told us to come and sit in front of the fire with him. He poured a whiskey and, with his pocketknife, cut biltong Ma had made the previous winter, dividing it equally between us, three half rashers on a sinew. Ma drank tea, never liquor. Pa said it was because of the sherries Ouma drank from lunchtime onwards.

"Now just look at this wonderful fire I made, isn't it magnificent? The logs are laid perfectly with not a hint of smoke. Most people are just too idiotic to do it right. It's really unbelievable how stupid people can be." I marvelled at how clever Pa was. Before he had to farm, he studied law and worked for Oom Faan Rorich typing summonses during university holidays. During his lunch hour he smoked cigarettes in the yard overlooking the jail. When Oom Paul died, Pa gave up his dreams and came to help Oupa on the farm.

"Tell me about your day," Pa said looking at Paul.

When Paul was excited he spoke with his hands. Ma said he conducted his sentences to closure just like Oupa Boetie used to. "The doctor was very interesting, I really liked speaking to her." Pa believed one must study something that you can fall back on, like law or engineering. Latin for matric because it is the foundation of all learning. Amo amas amat. Paul said he was going to be a writer one day.

Pa looked at him. "Is that so? Advice from a psychometrist no less?"

Pa's wonderful fire leapt and flickered. Pa sat in his armchair and Ma sat with Christiaan on her lap. The formal sitting room was for important occasions. It had a mohair carpet and an oil painting of a shipwreck along the coast of South-West Africa. There was a Chinese fire screen with geishas draped in red lacquer in the shade of cherry wood and crystal blooms. It was the most beautiful thing in our house, except for the porcelain bust of a lady on the server next to the Waterford crystal glasses. Pa bought them in Ireland years ago when he went with Oupa Boetie to select breeding bulls. One night a trapped and flustered owl flew up against the sideboard and everything shattered. The owl died and neither Selina nor Abram would touch the feathery corpse. Sothos believe that owls are a bad omen.

Christiaan and I lay under the seringa tree outside Ma's office. Berries bunched against the navy sky and weavers stacked nests potluck on the naked branches. Ma said when seringas come into flower they smell like wisteria with pepper added. Ma bought us tuisnywerheid jerseys, sold in plastic bags, that made you feel hot and cold at the same time. Mine was yellow and Christiaan's was green and Paul's had blue and brown stripes. She also bought a small pink one because there was going to be another baby.

Christiaan and I were sucking oranges we had softened on bricks and then poked a hole through with a stick. Selina and Stompie sat along the western wall eating samp and marog. Every winter Pa sent a wagon to collect bagged oranges from Groenebloem railway siding and all our labourers were given a sack. We kept our oranges in the drying room that stank of biltong blood. The orange juice burnt my swollen lips and my nose ran because of the dry winter air. Pa said we should be grateful for windstill days. When the wind came up, Pa sent home the workers who were harvesting in the peanut fields. That wind numbs the horizon and cuts like a knife into your kidneys. It pulls clouds across the sky, like mohair coming undone. Pa calls it a black southerly.

In the hallway the phone rang. Four long rings and four short ones. Christiaan and I stormed into the house, tripping over the cats on the doormat. Pa always screamed at us for running to the phone like feral animals just for the privilege of saying "double four zero four hello". I had to be more careful, because my new teeth were for life. Sometimes we eavesdropped when the neighbours made calls and they spoke about fertiliser and church.

It was Dr Cohen. I stood next to Ma. It was warm in Ma's office because Pa built our house to face perfectly north. Pa made scientific calculations on a matchbox so that it would be cool in summer and warm in winter. "What did she say?" Paul asked. "Let's talk when Pa comes for tea," Ma said.

Paul went back to the sofa and picked up *Black Beauty*. He said to Ma, "I can't believe they want to ban this." Paul loved using words that only grownups understood. After the expedition to Aandson that night Pa told Paul to stop showing off and imagining he was an adult. Ma agreed with Paul that the proposed ban was breathtakingly preposterous. I knew it was a story about a horse.

Christiaan and I crawled under the desk and sat colouring in pictures while Ma paid bills. He was four years younger than I was and did everything I told him. Ma put on a *Jakkals en Wolf* record. Christiaan and I felt sorry for Jakkals because his shifty plans always failed. Ma had lots of records. Maria Callas and Nana Mouskouri, and when Callas sang about love and dying from consumption, Ma would turn up the volume and Pa would turn it down and say, "She sounds delirious." If you forced some records to play backwards you could hear sinister messages laid down into the grooves by Satanists. Especially rock-and-roll bands from England. A man came to school and warned us about that. We all had to sit in the hall listening with our blazers on.

Ma crossed and uncrossed her long, stockinged legs under the table. Ma could draw money every month from the bank. Most women were on a strict budget from their husbands, but Pa always spoke about our money, not his money. In the beginning Ma wrote the date and the name on the cheque and then Pa signed. Now Ma paid all creditors and handled the banking, and sometimes she said, "Your father is a hopeless administrator."

Ma's office opened onto a courtyard. In summer people who came to see her waited under the seringa tree and in winter against the western wall. There was always someone. Young boys with dreams of university, so thin and nervous they needed sugared tea before they could speak, requests for school fees, funeral money, lifts to Klerksdorp, a matric dance dress, women in labour, toordokter accusations, ratels in the chicken coop. Sometimes there were also chancers.

Ma made a stained-glass window for her office to soften the afternoon sun. I lay in the yellow shaft with my tongue hanging out, pretending to be dying of tetanus. Ma and Paul ignored me. A swallow's nest was sifting fine sand down onto the carpet. Ma tolerated the nest, even though the swallows had made it inside. I gave up the pretence of dying when Pa came down to the house from the workshop for tea. We looked to see where he put his cap, because after tea we always had to find it. In summer we had to find the fly swatter so that Pa could spend the lunch hour cursing and swatting flies. Selina brought the tea. Christiaan and I grabbed some biscuits and Ma smacked our fingers.

"Dr Cohen has recommended that Paul goes to an English boarding school in Johannesburg." Pa sat in his chair across the room from us. Paul sat next to Ma. Outside the veld was singed black. A veldfire had come within reach of the house. Herons feasted on insects fleeing the burnt soil.

"Also, I must tell you that Kobus and Johnny won't be coming for holidays any more. Kobus's mother appeared out of nowhere and wants to live with him now that he has a job on the railways. With a

Standard Seven." Ma said, "He did well to get that far. Tomorrow we are going to Wolwefontein for slaughtering. And to tell Ouma Koeks the news of Paul going away."

Pa knocked his pipe against the leg of the chair. "I don't want you to get any funny ideas about where you come from. You will have to go to Grey College for high school."

"Yes Pa. I am grateful. I don't want to disappoint you. Thank you, Pa."

Once the crop on Rietpan had been brought in, cattle were sent to browse remnant stalks and husks in the lands. All winter trampling hooves hardened Pa's furrows. When the feed turned sparse, Cardow and the men drove the herd back across the district to Wolwefontein.

A thousand cattle set off before sunrise. The land between Wolwefontein and Rietpan is without contour. Men in blue overalls with balaclavas whistle and whip the herd in dawdling progress. The cattle kick up dust and bellow, skirting barbed-wire fencing along well-worn servitudes. By late afternoon lines of migrating geese lift the horizon and the cattle become obstinate.

We dropped Paul and Vusi off with Cardow at Blesboklaagte to help with the final stretch. A korhaan flew up from a patch of khakibos. Pa gave them a cane to share. He believed in the sweat of your brow.

Then we drove off to Wolwefontein. Pa grew up there. His great-great-great-grandfather Theuns Louis built a hartbeeshuisie during the Great Trek, and, after some orange harvests, a sandstone house with pressed ceilings. Ouma Koeks lived there alone because Oupa Boetie coughed himself to death in the bedroom at seventy-two from lung cancer. When Oupa was still alive he gave us mint crèmes from a hexagonal tube kept in his bedside table, if we ate our spinach. We still went there for lunch every Sunday. We ate roast lamb, roast potatoes and caramelised carrots on a small table in front of the fireplace. In summer there was a tapestry screen in the grate, and a clock hung in pride of place above the mantel that Oupa's uncle won at a fair a hundred years ago for shooting straight. On either side of the fireplace were oil paintings of Vytjie Bouwer and Willem Maseola.

Vytjie was a descendent of the Cape slaves. Grootoupagrootjie, our great-great-grandfather, made them sit for portraits and Vytjie would not remove her doek. Willem wore a jacket and a hat and he looked just like his grandson Champagne.

The English burnt the house down during the Boer War, but Ma says it was probably a pot left on the stove that caused the fire. The house was rebuilt in 1901 with sandstone quarried near the river. Stonemasons from Lesotho came to chisel and point. Posts and lintels held up the roof over a deep veranda where flyscreens banged to keep out insects. The pantry shelves were lined with aniseed rusks and preserved watermelon and there were hand-embroidered sheets in the linen press. Trellised vines from before the Boer War were wrapped in hessian to survive the frost. The yard was full of kapokkies and the orchard netted over to dishearten persistent flocks of weavers. Doves swirled above the chimneys before oncoming storms.

I liked the photographs in the hallway of the little girl in a ballet tutu and Pa and Oom Paul as babies, smiley in smocks. Paul said our ancestors were incredibly ugly. We put our suitcases in the spare room and went through for tea. We sat in front of the fire and Ouma held my hand. "Paultjie," she said, "you carry the family name and you must make us proud." Ma said Oupa Boetie had been an incredibly charming man, but he was hard on Pa. Very hard, especially after Oom Paul's death. The long hall framed a view towards Ouma's garden. There were English oaks, white stinkwoods, pepper trees and soft lawn covered in clover. In a bed of cannas was a sundial as memorial to Oom Paul. Beyond the old cattle kraal, silos filled with silage rose like turrets. On the horizon the ground fell into a canyon that carried the False River away.

The front garden used to open onto the wagon path between Bothaville and Kroonstad. That was years ago, before a road was tarred further to the north. We sold sand from the river for the slurry mix because we had the best quality sand. We had lots to be proud of.

Paul stood up. He winked at Vusi and me and we followed him out through the back kitchen and past the old stone kraal and silos.

Ma made us wear Ouma's bowling hat and Oupa's cap. We walked towards the river. Vusi was very happy because Pa gave him some pocket money for helping on the cattle drive. He had really good manners. He did things for Ma and Pa before they even asked. Pa said that is what considerate behaviour is all about, anticipating the needs of others.

In winter the air is as dry as paper. Waterbuck hid in riverine swags of wag-'n-bietjies and stinkwood. In summer the river could rise overnight and break its banks. It had lapped at the stoep of the house in living memory. Ouma's canna bed was planted on the hundred-year flood line.

We sat down in the shade of a stunted acacia on an outcrop of stone. The rocks were etched with faint drawings of eland, sable and ostriches. None of them could be found here any longer. Vusi and Paul took turns trying to shoot the Bushmen engravings with Paul's kettie. "Aren't you scared of going away to boarding school?" I asked Paul, tracing my fingers across a herd of running sable.

"Why should I be scared? At least I'll be getting away from Mr Kruger. I hate him. I really hate him."

Paul spat out the grass he was chewing. "Sometimes I hate Pa."

Vusi said, "Aikona Paul," pointing the kettie at him.

I wanted to go home. Bats swooped and darted through the thickening dusk. After dark, jackals cried like lost children near the river. During slaughtering time we always stayed over at Wolwefontein. Paul and I slept on single beds in the front room and Vusi slept on the floor. He brought his own blanket and a facecloth and towel. We had enamel bedpans under our beds to pee in the night. Christiaan slept with Ma and Pa in the room with faded dusky rose wallpaper. Once Nadia was born, she slept in a cot made up with lace on Ma's side of the bed.

The graveyard was too close to the opstal. The oregon floorboards in the passage warped and snapped as the temperature fell. The roof groaned. The wind moaned. Frost cracked. Some moths fluttered up against the old sash window. I did not want them to die of cold, so I got out of bed to open the sash window and let them in. I looked up and saw the angel from the graveyard at the window. My heart struggled like a trapped bird. The angel stood right up against the glass looking inside at us. I could hear his wings rustling as they scraped across the stoep floor. He spoke with the voice of an owl. I don't remember falling. Ma and Pa were bent over me. They took me to their room and I lay between them. For a long time I could still hear the angel breathing and Pa eventually said, "In God's name, stop this crap."

In the morning the angel was gone.

In winter there are no flies or mosquitoes and the cold prevents slaughtered carcasses from going off too quickly. The assembly line consisted of Ouma, Ma, Victoria, Pa, Champagne's son Andries and Likkewaan's son, Kort Piet. The line of people stretched out of the kitchen onto the lawn under the pepper trees. Guinea fowl had to hang for a few days for the meat to ripen. When ready, their festooned carcasses were pulled open, the purple skin and tendons audibly gave way. Fillets were cut with a thick seam of fat and laid head to toe in vats and layered in salt, to be hung up and dried as biltong for next winter. The kitchen table was covered in mincemeat and kneaded with cubed fat, coriander seeds, pepper and vinegar. Intestine sheaths were strapped over tap faucets to be cleaned, swelling as they filled with water. I helped Ma with the slippery intestines, laying the washed sheaths in enamel basins holding cold water. The flavoured mince was then funnelled into sausage makers and forced through the boiled, washed pigs' intestines. In the past, before meat could be frozen, they went around to neighbouring farms with karmenaadjies, the excess meat that would spoil before it could be eaten. That way every slaughtered ox in the district was consumed without waste. Ouma still resented some neighbours for only ever parting with the sparest of ribs.

Paul and Vusi helped Ma thread the fillets with disinfected metal hooks. Luckily the English hadn't burnt the ronddawel that had a cooling room buried underground where raw sausages and fillets were hung up to dry. The remaining carcass of meat hung over a large enamel basin that caught its dripping blood. Ouma's Labrador Pinky licked the blood off the cement floor and was constantly under Pa's feet. Pa said, "Ag Jesus Ma, please get rid of this damned dog." Ouma ignored him . He kept muttering under his breath about that ridiculous, hairy tub of lard and kicked Pinky when Ouma was not looking.

Old Anna went to make a fire beyond the kraal to boil tripe. She had rheumy eyes and casually stoked the intestines with their evil smell. She wore a wrapped blanket fastened with a big pin. She was scraping a boiled sheep's head with a blade to get rid of the hair. She muttered with her one tooth, "Food is food, food is food," holding out a sheep's eye and laughing. Paul walked up to her. He took the slippery orb from her hand, swallowed the eye whole. Anna stopped laughing and muttered approvingly. We walked away and Paul threw up into the prickly branches of a renosterbos.

We all went up to Johannesburg for Paul's first day at his new school. Paul went to say goodbye to Vusi and gave him his kettie. Ma took a Polaroid of Vusi and Paul standing against the Waaisand school wall. Paul in his St Peter's uniform and Vusi in his Rahohetswe uniform. They waved at the camera and said, "Goodbye Rietpan, goodbye." The front stoep of Waaisand Primary was made of clay and dung and smeared by hand. The farm women put their hands in hot water while they plastered dung floors to keep the consistency malleable and smooth. I told Vusi about my new cat. I named her Lietjiebet Lotriet. Pa had relented because of my puppy that a snake had killed, and I was allowed to keep her in my room. Lietjiebet was the name of the girl in a story that Ma had made up and I made her tell the story over and over. Lietjiebet was a very thin orphan covered in ash, just like my new kitten.

On the way to Johannesburg Ma and Pa sat in front, the three of us in the back seat and Paul's new school trunk in the boot. Nadia stayed at home with Selina. Pa lectured Paul about not forgetting his heritage. Pa said they always tried to build a bridge between the English and Afrikaans communities, just like his parents tried. There used to be great enmity and suspicion and very little mixing. Pa said he even used to believe, when he was at school, that English people did not know how to plough or ride a horse. When he thought about it now all the most successful farmers in the district have been English. Then Pa thought about his Ouma Miemie who was in the concentration camp in Bethulie. Her brother died there, but she held no bitterness. Pa muttered, "Those swine almost wiped us out and still expected us to fight on their side in the First World War."

At the entrance to the school Pa stopped the car and made Christiaan and me get out. He knelt down and said, "This is an important day for Paul. Don't speak Afrikaans until we leave. It will be embarrassing for him if you do." I was wearing closed shoes that pinched my feet and my favourite dress. It was made of pink Crimplene. There were many other boys and everyone knew each other. Christiaan and I sang "Bobbejaan klim die berg" to Paul when Ma and Pa were busy with registration. He gave us each a lammie. A boy came past and said, "Check the rock spiders." His friend sniggered. When we said goodbye to Paul on the steps of his new boarding house, I felt bad about "Bobbejaan klim die berg".

In the new school year there was no more Mrs Pearce and trying to find out where Paul was during break time. Ma and Pa left him there for six weeks. He wrote a poem about a car accident that appeared in the school yearbook. He cleared all the hurdles in the hundred-metre relay and won. He got into the cricket team. He joined the Philatelists' Society.

He wrote to us once a week during prep on a Wednesday. Dear Mum and Dad and the date. His left-handed letters still struggling to remain in place.

CHAPTER 5

I sat among the rustling stalks of opslagmielies with the voice of Meneer Louw in my head. "Unto the woman He said, I will greatly multiply thy sorrow and thy conception; in sorrow thou shalt bring forth children." It said so in Genesis printed onto soft and slender Bible pages heavy with abstraction and solemn import. Wind whipped at the tatty husks I had picked up to make corn dolls. Blood was running down my thigh. I tore some papery husks into strips and put them between my legs. Ma told me it would happen. I did not want to believe her.

"Unto the woman He said."

A dust devil sprang up and danced down the wenakker that girds the windbreak. An old ambulance was rotting away into scrap metal between the trees. Pa bought it years ago on auction as shelter for his sheepherders. Eventually the roof mouldered, the maroon cross on the doors peeled off, the stretcher bed cracked and tetanus lurked in the rusted chassis. That's where Paul hid his cigarettes.

I wiped my eyes, got up and walked towards the eucalyptus corridor at the edge of the pan. I saw Abram collecting firewood. We used wattle for firewood only when acacia ran out because blue gum burns too fast. "Is everything all right, kleinmies?" he asked, saw in hand and eyes downcast. "I hooked my leg on the barbed-wire fence," I said and started running home. I had hidden my stained panty in the bag full of mielie husks.

Threadbare milk muslins hung across the drying yard and Lietjiebet Lotriet lay asleep on winter sheets stacked on the ironing table. Mad Magdaleen hid the Sunlight bars for delicate fabrics. She was called mad because she hit her husband's girlfriends with a spade, praised Jehovah all day long and cursed die listige paradysslang. Blaming the serpent for the world's woes. Ma gave her a job because her husband's family chased her out of the house after he died from drinking skokiaan. Her in-laws said she had toored him. Ma said it's funny how most evil spells are cast on weekends.

I eventually found the Sunlight stash in an old ice-cream container on the top shelf of the laundry cupboard; used bars of soap too valuable for general use sagging and cracked like old shoes. I scrubbed the white cotton and the stain grew fainter but would not disappear. The water was too hot and my hands were too cold.

Ma had a very clever friend who had two doctorates and an even cleverer husband who said women's bodies are leaky and complicated. That's why you needed a special branch of medicine dedicated to their flaws. Gynaecologists. Ma kept going to see one in Klerksdorp to check on the stitch needed to keep the baby in after Ma fell off the pavement in town. Five children. I did not like to think of Ma and Pa doing that thing. When Ma told Paul she was pregnant again he just laughed and said she should try sleeping at the foot of the bed.

Mad Magdaleen walked into the laundry. She grabbed my arm and held it in the air. She danced on the spot then jabbed her other hand between my legs and said, "Now the man is going to come for this thing." She smacked her lips like she had eaten something delicious and hugged me to her chest. She was pyramid shaped and very tall and smelled of Zam-Buk. Then she smacked Lietjiebet Lotriet off the ironed sheets. I wriggled to get away from Magdaleen and took Lietjiebet upstairs to my bedroom.

Pa said my cat was a spoilt animal, with instincts too blunted to catch the damn rats in the ivy that Ma insisted on planting up the walls of the house. I lay on my bed watching the lonely mare whinnying along the paddock fence. She was iron coloured, like the pan in winter. Ma had blamed Pa for not buying her companions. When he eventually did, they kicked her lame. Wind scuffed the water, pleating froth in scalloped seams along the pan's southern edge.

I remember Ma saying your body has its own seasons, that the blood marks the end of your spring, but the beginning of your summer. Ma and Pa had gone to Harrismith to fetch Paul from the bus stop. Paul had been in high school for three years. After boarding school in Johannesburg, he followed his friends to high school in Natal. Pa's hopes for Grey College in Bloem came to naught. Ma says time flies and time stands still.

Magdaleen came to the door with a hotwater bottle and a glass of milk covered in a doily. She sat down on the bed, stroked my arm and asked me not to cry. "Hle Mamoosa, jy moenie huil." Black women used a folded cloth they washed and reused because there was no money for toiletries.

The day before Ma and Pa left to fetch Paul, an inspector from the Department of Bantu Affairs came to the farm. He wanted a list of names of people who were over sixty and no longer able to work. The elderly were to be repatriated to their Bantustans. "They need to be moved as they are no longer economically active," the man explained to Ma, standing next to her desk with his small feet and crooked heart. Ma asked him, "Would you dump your own mother in Holland, worse still, a fenced wasteland where she has no family or income, to slowly die of starvation and exposure in her old age?"

"Ag, mevroutjie," he said, folding and refolding his handkerchief, "the situations are not comparable."

"Just imagine," Ma said afterwards, "Abel and Mary went onto that list. What would happen to Wandi? Would Vusi have to look after him?"

Maureen got pregnant just after Abel became headmaster at Waai-sand. Mary came with the news of Maureen's condition and lay on Ma's lap weeping. Maureen was only seventeen then and would not say who the father was. In Ma's day, if an unmarried woman got pregnant it was best she killed herself. Black people don't mind as much about that. Abel and Mary later raised Maureen's son Wandi because Maureen had finished matric and won a grant to study in America. The day Abel and Mary brought word of the scholarship Pa grabbed Maureen by the waist and waltzed her up and down the entrance hall out onto the lawn and they polkaed all the way to the pan's edge and collapsed laughing. Then he opened some wine and got the atlas out to find Pennsylvania on the map and even Abel had a sip of alcohol. Mary dabbed her eyes with an embroidered handkerchief. She kept saying, "Morena," which means God in Sesotho. Ma gave Maureen a warm coat she had bought in Johannesburg years ago for an undis-closed amount. It was lined with fur and floor length and felt as soft as Lietjiebet Lotriet. Pa said winter in America was far colder than a July day with a black southerly blowing. He went there once with some other farmers to look at mielies and came home with tales of rich, black topsoil that is twelve feet thick and women who sold themselves on street corners.

The blood made me feel dirty and ashamed. When Ma came home that night I told her about the blood and she promised not to tell anybody. The next morning Pa brought roses from town held together by a satin ribbon. He kissed me on the forehead and congratulated me on becoming a woman. I decided never to tell Ma a secret again.

Every morning Selina laid the table for breakfast with jams on a tray and serviettes in rings. Pa liked his marmalade to be refilled into an opaque ceramic pot he bought in England years ago that said *Cooper's marmalade made by Royal appointment for the Queen* in blue glazed ink. Selina refilled it from the canned marmalade Ma bought at Allem Brothers. Pa and Ma were going in to town after breakfast to lay a complaint about the Bantu Affairs official. Sometimes people in Johannesburg could help. Ma also had to do the licensing for our wagons and tractors at the municipal offices. Pa believed you must give unto Caesar what is due unto Caesar, even if he is a heartless shit. The tax on the licensing paid for the upkeep of provincial roads.

Paul and Vusi were made to work on the land. Paul spent all day driving a tractor and his face went from pale to red to dark brown. Paul and Pa left before sunrise and when they came in for breakfast Paul held a book under the tablecloth and read surreptitiously.

Pa said, "Put the book away."

Ma dished up from the serving table and I handed the plates to Pa and the boys. Paul sat on his book. Pa insisted on warm plates and fresh toast and three-minute eggs. He has been showing Selina how to crack an egg every morning since I can remember. Ma glanced at Paul in the mirrored mantelpiece that also came from Barney Barnato's demolished mansion in Parktown. It formed part of the haul gifted to us through Nationalist spite. Whenever Pa looked up and saw the carved teak mantelpiece, he would get angry all over again and rail about vandals and criminals.

"Can you believe that presumptuous inspector arsehole went to the stat before he came up to the house?" Pa said to Ma. "Goldberg was just telling me this morning. Snooping around on private property. The audacity of it. He must not come and tell me the law is on his side. He'd better learn some basic manners or he will leave with fewer teeth if he has the gall to trespass on my property again."

I put down his plate with scrambled eggs and chops. "Get me the Worcester sauce," he said.

"Surplus people removal. Christ. Every one of those bastards sitting in cabinet is responsible for passing these laws. I will just reinstate all the pensioners as employees. Give them a contract. Then let's see how they legislate their way round that."

Paul started reading again and Pa buttered his toast. The butter curls leisurely unmoulded on the hot bread.

Pa said, "What's so bloody interesting that you can't talk to us about? Hey?" He took the book from Paul's lap and jammed it between his gymnastic trophies on the sideboard. The pommel horse and high bar used to be Pa's disciplines. In the photographs of competitions he took part in way back Pa's face was shiny and open and his head full of hair.

In August a grey westerly stirs in the Kalahari and blows east for months. It plays handmaiden to fires. Its hands and feet are grit and tumbleweed and midday is its bleak, abandoned heart. Ma complained that dusting this time of year was a Sisyphean bore.

Pa leaned back and said, "Your mother's moans about the weather make me think of that American visitor who came to see old Jock Evans in the fifties when all the roads were still dirt tracks. Apparently the American looked at him and said, 'Jock, is this featureless howling waste the country you fought the Boers for?' Apparently, when Jock nodded, the American said, 'Can't you fight them again, and force them to take it back?'"

Paul smiled.

"Of course," Pa said, "the beauty of our part of the world is that the wind always dies down by sunset. Then you can sit on the stoep and enjoy a drink. That American never saw it after the rains when another country arises from the water's providence."

Pa stood up and folded his napkin. "I don't think your mother and I will be back for lunch. Finish off and get back to the lands."

Ma kissed Paul on the head and then rested her arm on his shoulder. "Remember yourself," she said and left.

Paul looked at me. "At least we will be spared the hypocrisy of saying grace."

"I believe in God," I said.

"Of course you do." He smiled at me.

Paul got up and stood leaning against the window looking out at the pan. He tapped his fingers on the glass. The boys in my class were much smaller than Paul and they played marbles during break and one of them wrote me a letter saying *roses are red, violets are blue, i love you, will you love me too*? I had thrown the letter out of the moving car on the way from school and watched it flutter like a dead moth decanted from a dusty lampshade.

I started stacking the plates. "These August winds drive everybody nuts. Pa said so. Did you know that Tannie Mariet's neighbour shot his wife and then himself last week? He killed her, shattered his own jawbone and now he is in hospital waiting to go to prison. Apparently he told her a thousand times to get the rattling windows fixed." Tannie Mariet smoked thin menthol cigarettes, was always on a diet and helped Ma with the accounts on Mondays.

Paul looked at me. "I'd better get back to the lands before Andries gets home." Paul called Pa by his first name when he was not around.

"I am going to help Selina with the butter," I said as he pulled the kitchen door closed. Ma called it a happy door because of the red and green glass in the casement openings.

Selina had started churning cream from Wolwefontein and asked me to wipe the counter. Wolwefontein was too far from town to rely on bought milk and Ouma sent cream in Consol glass jars once a week. Lang Piet still turned the crank of the cream separator by hand every afternoon, while biltong cured slowly in the cellar below his feet and shadows lengthened toward the river. We had a dairy at Aandson across the tar road from Rietpan. Abram used to hitch a small wagon to the milk tractor before dawn and sometimes we trundled along under smudged stars, rolled up in blankets. Frieslands lumbered into the milkshed with full udders and Abram greased their teats from a pot of lanolin. We watched him work amidst the stench of dung, hot milk and wet snouts swagged with spittle. Filled milk cans were clanked shut with a lid and carried onto the wagon. Cows were shooed back into the paddock while clouds of queleas roused the last of the sleeping calves. Then we rattled back home with the sky still doused in rosewater. Pa put a stop to the Aandson dairy because of all the hassle. Now we bought milk in town.

Selina and I smoothed the surface with wooden spoons before we packed the ice-cream containers filled with fresh butter into the freezer. The seasons imbue butter and egg yolks with pigment, quickening to a ripe yellow in summer from all the new grass. In winter, butter was as faded as frost. Selina pulled a mound of curls off the last block that she kept inside the fridge in a stone pot.

I went upstairs to practise scales because I was playing an exam later in the year. It was a new piano from Klerksdorp that Mrs van der Westhuizen had helped us choose. The old piano went down to the coast to Plettenberg Bay where Pa and Ma had bought a house overlooking the sea. An ark of our second-hand things rattled down to the coast on a mielie truck. Three ball-and-claw armchairs from Ouma Koeks. Tired mattresses. Wolwefontein's paraffin fridge. The piano was wrapped in blankets and fastened so securely by Pa they needed the police on the other side to set it free. It still had Paul's inking on middle C, although the ivory sheaves were being lifted off by sea air laden with corrosive salt crystals. Curtain rails, braai grids, car engines – anything metallic – were gradually ruined by a sallow-winged mist that came in drifts at dawn. A prevailing shore wind pulled the strings out of tune. Every holiday an old, blind tuner from George came with his coloured driver and went ping-ping on his tuning fork to make it good for another year.

I slumped on my piano stool at the thought of the wearying climb from c to c with all the majors and minors and chromatics in between. I placed my fingers on the keys and went up and down, two octaves each, first the right hand, then the left hand, then together and the afternoon disappeared andante cantabile into the piano, at a swift walking pace with a singing effect.

From the uneven coaxing of sound came other places, snow covered and candelit, other voices curling up church naves like smoke in winter, streaming into my sash window that Pa saved from the demolition yard. Ma came home from town and said she wished she could personally string up the Nationalists by the neck on village squares throughout the land.

When Maureen's letters arrived from America, Abel and Mary drove very slowly in their car down the driveway, softly over the middelmannetjie, to come and share her news. I knew the sound that everyone's car made over the cattle grid. Pa charged his bakkie in two by two, like the rigid march in my European folk music book with soldiers in pointy hats and golden lapels. Abel and Mary drove a tentative barcarolle over the cattle grid in six-eight time. With Ma it depended on her mood, a quick waltz charging out, or a lazy one driving back, eating koeksisters in the car to finish before Pa saw.

A big peach tree flourished at the entrance gate. We never saw its fruit because children from the stat plucked the ripe peaches at night. When the tree blossomed Ma drove as slowly as Abel and Mary and we lolled out the windows, dazed by the silky shoots adorning the pitted branches.

Maureen's letters came in soft par avion envelopes, written on crinkly blue sheets. Maureen wrote that she was lonely and missed the township most of all. I could not understand how that was possible. She was lucky to get away. Mr Kruger used to tell us, "You'd better study hard. For each white person, ten kaffirs are standing by to take your place in the job market one day." Ma said true loneliness is being alone amidst your own people.

Abel and Mary brought a visitor along with Maureen's latest letter. He was the new school inspector for the district. Mary and Ma wanted to arrange friendship teas between the black and white communities, to help cross the divide of the district road. Ma said we needed to reach out to each other in our own towns. Otherwise the country was going to go up in flames. Abel said he would identify suitable people in the township.

"Good morning Mr Botha, my name is Ishmael Mabitle." I had never heard black people call white people mister or misses. It was always baas or miesies. Selina brought tea and we sat in the formal sitting room while Abel and Pa spoke and Ishmael listened. Abel wanted to have a prayer meeting. He said the young people are suspicious of whites. Pa must try to understand.

Pa jumped up, "I am not white."

Abel and Mary laughed and Ishmael's cup rattled in his hand.

Pa made me fetch a book from his office called *Groep sonder Grense* that traced the bloodlines of the major Afrikaans families. A minister was suing the writer for defamation. Pa held out the book to Ishmael, "Just have a look. I am not even of mixed race, the Bothas are pure Griekwa!"

Ishmael drank tea with three sugars. Ma always told us that black people had perfect teeth because they could not afford sweets, but sugar was a type of sweet and black people always drank lots of sugar in their tea. Pa kept jumping up with the fly swatter. He covered the cream and jams in doilies and told Ma not to keep the cosy off the pot too long. Nadia climbed onto the sofa and sat on Ishmael's lap. She put her rusk in his tea and then made him have a bite.

Pa said to Ishmael, "So Mr Mabitle, what say you? Are we going to do this?"

Ishmael cleared his throat. "I want to tell you Mr and Mrs Botha that I came here today unwillingly but out of respect for Abel Dlamini. I made a promise to myself many years ago never to be friends with a white person."

Pa sat looking down at the carpet and stirred his tea.

Ishmael continued, "But I do not want to live a life forged in hate. Then I am no different to those who hate me without knowing me."

Ishmael looked at Pa.

I thought about the fight at school that week in class. Juffrou went to the staff room and Esmarie Coetzer stood up and said the NP was giving away the country to the kaffirs. To think Dingaan's impis swung baby Voortrekkers against the wheels of the wagons splitting open their soft heads, and now we want to give the country to them. The children whose parents stayed behind in the NP kept quiet. I kept wishing Juffrou would come back. Our family were considered to be communists, an accusation so grave that no-one dared say it out loud. Juffrou said in her day black people were called Outa and Ousie as a sign of respect. She had old-fashioned values, but she would not share a teacup with a black person.

When they stood up to go, Ishmael thanked Pa in Afrikaans for his hospitality. Pa grinned with pleasure. Pa's teeth were going yellow from the smoking.

Our television room was on the landing with books in one corner and Ma's sewing machine and fabrics in the other corner. Butterick, Vogue and Mayberry patterns gathered dust above the windowsill. Clothes could be cheaply imported from China so now Ma used the machine mainly for tailoring and mending. On Saturday afternoons, while Pa and the boys were watching rugby, she oiled and threaded her machine. During half-time, I would go downstairs with her to make tea for everyone. Sometimes they shouted so loudly during matches that the doves scuttled into flight from the skylight.

Pa came to the kitchen. "Bring some biltong," he said checking for his knife on his belt holster. He walked back upstairs to the TV room carrying his glass of whiskey and clinking ice. Today, the Prime Minister was going to give an important speech on television. Our neighbours the Swanepoels came over because they still did not have a TV. They were very religious and worried. Ma said they were decent people. Ma and Pa and Mr and Mrs Swanepoel sat on the sofa,

Christiaan and I sat on the floor and Paul stood behind the sofa watching. Ma and Pa were hopeful that change was in the offing. Eventually Pa said, "Hierdie fokken Botha maak ons hele familie se naam gat;" Mrs Swanepoel clutched the collar of her appliquéd blouse.

"There goes our currency," Ma said quietly.

Ma and Pa walked our visitors out to their car. I watched from the window as they bunkered down in the cold. Paul stood next to me. "Shame," he said, "those Swanepoels don't want to believe that the Ooms in the NP don't have their best interests at heart."

"What's a Rubicon?" I asked Paul.

"Do you know what the problem is with these fucking fascists? Even the ugly ones. They are stylish, man. Check the Nazis, those suits they wore were the thing. Those cunts understood how to dress. The right understands that violence is sexy. Lefties are just too soft cock. A Rubicon, Sliminique, is the vantage point from which you can only gain hindsight."

Paul walked to his room and slammed the door. Christiaan took his Meccano tractor and went to bed. Ma and Pa stood in the entrance hall. I heard Pa whispering to Ma. "Sending the children away might save them from the Broederbonders. I know it's not how we planned it, but it could open up the world for them." They sat down on the wide bottom step of the teak staircase in the dark. Pa held Ma's hand. "Just think," he said. "I wanted to work on a ship after school. To see the world. My father would not let me. Would it not be wonderful if our children could be citizens of the world?"

There was a girls' school near Paul's English private boarding school in Natal. A satellite for sisters of Hilton boys. They posted a set of papers. I wrote the entrance exam in the NG church hall in Viljoenskroon with the district inspector invigilating. I finished the sections quickly and watched him sitting in a shaft of afternoon sunlight, absent-mindedly eating his snot.

I did not really want to leave. I had become head girl at Salomon Senekal Primary despite Ma and Pa's politics. Ma said she almost fainted with disbelief when she heard I had been elected. I wore a tight vest under my school dress every day to flatten the swelling of my breasts. Then I pinned my golden head-girl badge so that it would lie straight. I shaved the hairs growing between my legs with one of Pa's razors that I stole and hid in my shoe cupboard. Sometimes I wished I could die if growing up was going to be as humiliating as this. The rest of the time I was grateful for being alive and prayed to God thanking Him every night. I felt He was on our side and that everything would come right, trusting the wise words of President Brand who in 1875 signed the title deed to Rietpan. I know that Ma did not really like those schools in Natal. She said that English South Africans think they are better than us. Paul said Ma just had working-class hang-ups.

Harvesting continued into the night. Cardow, Goldberg, Champagne, September and Geswind in their blue overalls and balaclavas took turns driving the combines. Amidst the musky smell of shredded starch clanging onto cold metal, they fed acacia branches into konkas for warmth, rolling tobacco cigarettes with softened newspaper. Vusi and Paul drove wagons that carried the maize away to the silos in the morning. Their wagonloads bore weight and witness to proficient planning within the vagaries of weather.

Goldberg told me that when Paul and Vusi dropped the casuals off in the location, they bought quarts at the shebeen. He spoke in front of Paul and shook his head and clicked his tongue. "Oorlog will be very angry that you are drinking beer," he said. Paul hugged the much smaller older man to his chest and said, "Oorlog won't know a thing." Only rich men drank quarts. Selina brewed beer in big enamel vats that fermented outside her house and sometimes the pig broke through her ogiesdraad enclosure and washed down her litter with beer. The cannibalistic sow collapsed onto the road snoring with ice-white hair heaving like an old man's whiskers on her big belly.

The post brought news from the school in Natal that I had won the major scholarship. Ma ran up the stairs with the news. In her hand, she also had Paul's school magazine, containing an essay he wrote. Pa danced me up and down the passage. "What a proud day for our family," he said. "Life stretches ahead full of wonderful expectation for you children," Pa said, putting his arm around me. He poured a whiskey and Ma made tea and then she read Paul's essay to us.

My story by Paul Botha (Form 4)

He was brought to the air by a surgeon's blade across his mother's swollen stomach while the rain swept dust from the farmlands and clattered on the huddled traffic in the city's streets. Through the forgotten years he found feet and speech and hearing, amazed in the fashion of children, by the soft calling of doves and early morning gunshots, by the strange rhythms that sounded from distant khayas and the crash of thunder in the peaceful night, the years of hide-and-seek in prickly pear orchards, of first reluctant friends and of playing quietly below the flow of adult conversation. Time passed as a hazy succession of seasons, of frost on the lawn and slow summer afternoons and mulberries staining his cheeks in the spring. With autumn came the games in the mielie wagons and and the smells of harvesting.

The following year they bought him a uniform and hard, uncomfortable shoes to wear to school. He was wary of sideburned men, stern as granite, and the dark threat of canes they represented. His pencil strayed too often, so the lady, the one who sat in the front of the classroom, kept him during break times while the other children went out to the playground. He hid his embarrassment but with the cruelty of children they drew it out and surrounded him. He spilt stinging tears on some quiet stairway until they found him and chased him up. His writing deteriorated so that the teacher threatened to make him repeat the year. He searched for shelter in his hopeless tears but found none. The next year brought no hope, and the parents of the slim child went to a specialist in the city who gave greybeard and grave advice upon which different school clothes were bought and he began boarding in the city. It was a colder climate but he discovered warmth in books and the children were only different in that they spoke another language.

Home became a station and the sounds and sights reluctant memories. He became a stranger to childhood hideouts and once familiar haunts. He stayed in his room, absorbed by tales of paper people and lands of ink so that the land beyond his windowsill faded in memory. He was a series of retreats, shelved emotions and stunted confidences. The drive home was quiet, Ma was reminiscing about something or other, and his eyes followed the cold night road home. They expected him to begin working on the farm that holiday and he resented the intrusion. His indignation drove his father to quiet fury. Ma took to pleading in her diplomatic fashion. He remained on his side of the wall and bitterly stumbled deeper into the labyrinth of his frustration. He could find no justification for his stubbornness; reason evaded him on occasions like these and he could never stem the iron veil of tears that inevitably descended to shut him out.

He was woken the next morning, before the sun had risen, by his father, he was going to work in the lands, whether he liked it or not. He sat sullenly through the drive to the lands. There he was left alone in charge of a Sotho labourer who hovered about apologetically. He stood in the gathering morning light and stared at the tractor driver through his tears. The man helped him onto the tractor and then started it. He pulled a lever and drove the ploughshares into the heavy soil. After their first few rumbling passages the sun began to warm their hands and faces and the rich smell of ploughed earth lay open to the air. The day was hot and, when his father fetched him, dust was clinging to his face and he felt weary, but the trip seemed shorter than the morning's journey. He returned for weeks until all the ploughing had been done. One Sunday night, it was nearly full moon; there was a knock on the backdoor. On opening he discovered a barefoot herd boy, breathless with the news of strayed cattle. It took several hours to round the animals up and he was tired from the day's activities. His father started the car but he declined the ride. "Thanks Pa, but I would like to walk." The moon cast a cool light on the quiet landscape and the night breeze flushed his cheeks.

He walked home whistling, feet touching firmly on the earth.

CHAPTER 6

Pa took us in the station wagon. Paul back to Hilton, another foot taller, and me with newly straightened teeth. We drove through a flat expanse of tilled land and verges crowded in lilac and ivory blooms. Cosmos had spread along campaign trails of the Boer War as a chance traveller in oats brought in from South America for the English cavalry. "Boerperde could graze on the veld, but the Brits pampered their horses with imported feed," Pa explained.

The road spilt down slopes the colour of glossy starlings. Paperbark acacias flecked stretching plains. "O die groen, groen land van Natal," Pa sang off key from the FAK songbook about the province and its verdant hills. We stopped at a picnic spot with concrete tables and half-moon seats. Pa took out the Tupperware and coffee flask. Cold chicken and blue eggs. Salt and pepper in tinfoil sachets. Rusks in a tin and a jammerlappie in a separate packet. Pa finished his coffee and lit up a cigarette. Paul and I looked at each other. Pa gave up smoking years ago.

"Spioenkop," Pa said, pointing to stacked hills in the blue distance. "Your mother's family, the Erasmusse, distinguished themselves there by all dying."

Paul laughed at Pa. "Ouma Celia says the Bothas distinguished themselves by surrendering before the first shot was fired."

Pa sucked hard on his cigarette. "Your Ouma has too many opinions." That was a character flaw in Pa's book.

He stepped on his cigarette butt and we got back on the road, passing towns named after pork sausages and unfamiliar battles. Paul was wearing a black blazer, a striped tie, shiny shoes and a new haircut. His Number Ones. I worried about my inadequate English. My trunk was filled with an unfamiliar vocabulary of bloomers, blues, house ties, tuck and mufti.

Pa drove past a speed trap set behind an oleander hedge. He commiserated with black drivers who were always being harassed by the traffic police. We drove away penalised. Pa swore about having to find money to pay the fine and I offered him my birthday savings. I kept coins inside a music box underneath a twirling plastic ballerina, who pirouetted until her carousel ran out of jingles teased with metallic teeth from a winding cog. "Nonsense, you love worrying. I have money to pay that hillbilly, I just don't feel like it."

We passed green lakes and blue forests with smoke drawling up distant valleys. A gloved guard waved us through the pillared entrance into the oak-squired avenues of Hilton College. Fondant gables, lilied fountains and pea-green lawns swung past. There was a chapel consecrated in iceberg roses. Pine needles scented flagstone paths. I wondered if the word *dapples* was made up from shadow and apples. The grounds tapered into bush full of blue monkeys and oribis. It was the most beautiful place I had ever seen. I disliked it immediately.

According to Pa, the English founded these schools on the hills above Pietermaritzburg after they chased the Boers back over the Drakensberg and the Zulus beyond the Tugela. "Probably thought they'd find gold here, the avaricious bastards." Paul's boarding house was called Newnhams.

Pa greeted the housemaster and Paul leant into the car. "Don't look so stricken. Your boet is looking out for you. Watch out for lesbians, though." He laughed and waved goodbye. The word made me blush. I knew it was about pornography, which was even worse to think about than periods.

Hilton College receded into a conifer haze, supplanted by the outlines of an English village like I had seen on Ouma Koeks's cake tins. Pa knew all about engineering and architecture. Everything fascinated him, from the pyramids to the Alhambra to the mock Tudor Hotel we stopped to inspect. He smoked a last cigarette, admiring beams and trusses and wondering whether they were structural.

Further along barley twist chimneys rose on the roofs of St Anne's Diocesan College for Girls above a clipped hedge. Gravel scrunched as we drove in. Pa said, "Heavens alive, how beautiful."

We stepped onto a carpet of magenta cherries and I took Pa's hand. "I'm scared."

Pa folded my arm into his. "It's perfectly natural to feel afraid. Whenever the first wagonload of maize goes in for weighing, I feel nervous. Or at university when I did a big salto during gymnastics competitions."

The school faced a small valley with outstretched arms and trimmed lawns cambering down to forest. The very pale school chaplain welcomed us. I knew the right English word for his skin colour: *translucent*. Tea was served in the shade of a Cape chestnut on white cloths showing only the ankles of trestles laden with custard slices, sandwiches shorn of crusts and pastries cooked with apples and raisins. Pa said the spread was fit for a wedding.

The headmaster made his welcoming speech in a long hall darkened by yards of burgundy velvet curtains. Windows alternated with honour rolls scrolled in goldleaf onto gabled panels. *Head girl, Dux, Deportment Prize.* Pa studied the walls. The headmaster shared the stage with a grand piano. In Viljoenskroon there was one in Mrs van der Westhuizen's house and another in the NG church hall where exams were played twice a year under the exacting judgement of Unisa professors. "I implore parents not to contact their daughters for the first few weeks. Comply for their sake," the headmaster said.

"I suspect that Irish brogue is lending his words a greater charm than they merit," Pa mumbled. My dress hung lower than everyone else's. Pa had loved boarding school. "Grey College, those were wonderful years. That would have been better. Bloemfontein. Maar nou ja, as a result of your brother's theatrics you are here now."

My allotted boarding house, Mollie Stone, lay beyond the horseshoe of school proper off to the left, like a discarded shoe. A pretty one, though. Pa almost had a conniption fit when he saw the intricately tiled veranda. "One day," he said, "I would like to tile the front stoep on Wolwefontein like this. Just imagine."

I wanted to go with Pa. I could not bring myself to say goodbye. He had a long drive back to the Free State and it was planting season. Ma was home with Christiaan and Nadia and the new baby. We called him Boetie. He was born early, despite the stitch, then went yellow and got rickets. Selina had to take him into the garden every morning like a potted sunflower to get some sun.

Pa wound down the window as he drove away in our old Mercedes shouting, "We love you, Nonsense. We're very proud of you."

Poppies with pollen navels shivered next to my window on hairy stems. The last of the afternoon sun lit them up like candles made of lemon peel. I sat on my unpacked trunk waiting for dinner. A girl with her skirt hitched up came into the dormitory and said, "You're that girl from Viljoens ... uhm ... Viljoenskraal or whatever, who won the scholarship?" Everyone giggled. "Welcome to the house of ill repute. That's the dinner bell. Catch a wake up."

I followed them to the dining hall. Prefects stood guard in the corridors. Speaking was forbidden. The stench of boiled cabbage seeped from an enormous room where conversations barrelled up to the rafters. A teacher rang a brass bell and shouted, "Girls, girls! Quiet!" Heads were bowed to "for what we are about to receive" and then the clattering resumed.

Zulu kitchen staff delivered meat floating in metal trays. The matric at the head of the table made her selection and sent the dishes down along a hierarchy of age. Yorkshire pudding, bubble and squeak, toad-in-the-hole. Salt came in glass bottles mixed with dry rice to prevent caking. Sneeze pepper looked like finely ground gravel. The girls were tall and big with breasts and acne. All the black girls sat together and all the Indian girls sat together and all the white girls sat together. Ma said it would be wonderful because people got to mix here in a natural way. I ate nothing. High up in the far corner, bats hung like dead fruit from a beam. I imagined them, once the hall was deserted, swooping and tracing their arcane pathways through the vaulted dark. Dinner ended with another tolling bell. Walking across the lawn after meals was a privilege reserved for those in Standard Six. The smell of anthracite grew wet and bloomed in the descending mist. A hadeda poked around in failed song.

After lights out, I crept out of the dormitory and sat in the bathroom crying softly. Mist swallowed sound, but smells came from everywhere. Disinfected drains, waxed corridors, sweating shoes, ripening socks, tired sofas and unloved carpets.

"What is this all about?"

Mrs Motherway stood in the doorway with her legs crossed, smoking a cigarette from a tortoiseshell filter. She was our housemistress from Zimbabwe, but she called it Rhodesia. She had a helmet of grey hair and the voice of a man. "Let me tell you about tears, my girlie. Come with me." I reluctantly followed into her small annex next to the common room and sat on her sherbet green couch, careful not to dishevel crocheted doilies protecting the armrests. On the wall three ceramic mallards flew towards a picture rail. She poured herself a drink and slugged it back. "Both my boys died in the bush war. Both soldiers. And for what?" I looked at the row of tonic bottles with yellow stickers peeling away from the wet glass. Pa says quinine helps against malarial mosquitos. "I lay in bed with a gun to my head for a whole year." She turned and looked at me. "I lacked the courage to live or die. So girlie, save your tears for when you really need them. Now go to bed."

Weather was determined by what the girls called The Berg. Their G's entered decorously and shut the door, not like in Afrikaans where they come like dragged chairs scraping over a tongue paved with bricks. In summer the hot wind grated tempers and in winter cut like a sore tooth. I continued to walk the corridors at night, deflecting Mrs Motherway and the prefect who made me massage her back after lights out and wash her knickers on Sundays. Mrs Motherway discovered the Lonely Hearts corner in newspapers and I was singled out for the role of abject scribe. "What does it mean?" she hovered eagerly as I translated advertisements from potential suitors on long Saturday afternoons. *Die liefde van God vind uiting in die liefde tussen 'n man en 'n vrou. Blank en Christen. Geen vetgatte asseblief.* A preference for thin, Christian whites. I preferred Mrs Motherway with her gun and gin and dating service to the matric after lights out.

During break I sat on a footstool in our common room, drinking tea from an enamel mug marked *Dominique Botha*. Anything not claimed went missing. Mrs Motherway said all this stealing by spoilt brats was a disgrace. Botha was mispronounced as a given, the middle consonant sliding with no hint of a glottal stop. It was the same surname as the Prime Minister and Minister of Foreign Affairs. That fact was met with, "What? Who? What is a Prime Minister?" The consensus in the common room was that companies queued outside our wrought-iron gates for the privilege of employing St Anne's girls. Such was the quality and breadth of our education.

Tamara Williams stood up on the sofa and said, "I don't give a shit about university or a job, do you think Prince Edward will marry me because I am a St Anne's girl?" She pushed her breasts together and pouted and the room erupted in laughter. Mrs Motherway screamed from next door, "Shuddup and behave. Your parents want you to grow up to become ladies."

I wished away the days. I memorised the periodic table and irregular French verbs. I scaled marathons across tattered keys in a music room the size of a single bed. There was one small window framing crows scavenging off the kitchen rubbish nearby and a poster of Beethoven fading against the wall.

At last the curfew was lifted and Paul came to visit. On Sunday afternoons Hilton boys could walk twelve conifer-lined kilometres in their Number Ones to sit on the front lawn at St Anne's from two to five. I waited for him at the entrance gates, building mounds with lilli pilli berries and memorising THE BOOK. We were to write a test on the matrics and their pets and boyfriends, if they had them. THE BOOK had to be copied in Koki and every consecutive letter written in a different colour.

Paul arrived with two friends. "Jesus," he said, "why are you so thin? Ma is going to freak when she sees you." At least the bleeding had disappeared, I thought. The freckled friend said, "Hey Blitz, your sister looks just like you." James and Adi. I remembered them from Paul's school in Johannesburg but they were much bigger now. Paul was called Blitz because he ran like lightning when he got the ball. First-team rugby players were entitled to a scarf that hung like a luminous wreath around the necks of the anointed few. St Anne's girls were given special permission, called exeats, to watch Hilton and Michaelhouse play rugby. Hilton and Michaelhouse boys did not get special exeats on St Anne's sports days. Fiona's mother said it trained girls from a young age to accept that men play golf on weekends. Pa did not play golf. He worked on Saturdays. During the Currie Cup he watched all the games and the Orange Free State team never ceased to disappoint him. "'ovs' stands for 'Ons Verloor Saterdag'. Verdomp."

We went and sat on the lawn and Paul lay on my lap. He complained about my poking hipbones, folded his blazer into a pillow and settled down on the grass instead. James kept smiling at me and asked what subjects I was doing. "We only choose our matric subjects in Form Four," I said. I felt an involuntary blush blooming along my throat.

"What subjects are you doing?" I asked.

"James's favourite subject," Paul said, "is the female race. Except he's not doing any of them."

James laughed and reddened under his freckles, "Ja, old Blitz schemes he is quite the Romeo."

Paul turned onto his back and plucked a blade of grass to chew. "Please tell me Fiona Stanley is in your house?" He grabbed his crotch and said, "Jesus, that girl is hotter than Durban."

"She's in my class and she is my friend."

"Excellent," Paul said. "You may eventually prove to be of some use to me."

Adi did not speak. He wore a black armband stitched onto his blazer sleeve. James asked, "Are those the Michaelhouse mourning colours for always losing against Hilton?" Adi smiled, "I wear it in commemoration of June 16th." Adi and Paul had joined the End Conscription Campaign and went down to Pietermaritzburg to listen to speeches. That's how they became friends. There was an objector in Kroonstad penitentiary who had been sentenced to six years. We used to drive past the jail on the way to my ballet exams when I was still at Salomon Senekal Laerskool.

The tall blondes from the Molly Stone common room came to pay a protracted homage under the oak tree. "Dominique is so adorable, I didn't know she was your sister, Paul." I stared at my shoes. Victoria and Venetia laughed at everything Paul said.

I looked up at pines that held the memory of winter in their creviced barks. I willed time to pass slowly. I watched a sacred ibis flock take wing. Theirs was a daily migration. There must be water nearby, perhaps jaçanas, lilies and gallinules like in the vlei back home. I could only guess. We were hemmed in by walls, surrounded by strangers, encircled by midlands, buttressed by foothills where a winding road climbed west and unravelled into smaller and thinner threads on the map, eventually fraying into the dust road that led home. The flight of the ibises meant taking leave. We walked to the gate and I clung to Paul and started crying. He gestured to James and Adi to walk on. I sobbed into his chest, onto his collared shirt, onto his first-team scarf and academic colours. "I know I am lucky to be here, but I really hate this place."

He took me into his arms. "You're just homesick, it's normal. When I first went to boarding school in Johannesburg I dreamt of running away every night. I wanted to walk home. Once I even got as far as Rosebank and a garage attendant took me back to school. He broke curfew to do that."

I wiped my eyes with my hands, "I dream about home every night. I can fly in my dreams. I always get as far as the peach tree and then the sun starts rising and I am pulled back here. My feet never touch the ground on the other side."

He smiled. "It gets better. Soon you will be sick of home. I better go before those pedants punish me for desertion."

That night one of the Malawians woke me up after evensong. Her father was a missionary who lived in the middle of nowhere near an enormous lake. "Stand guard at the door," she said climbing onto my bed. She unscrewed the burglar bars on the window above the fire escape. "Where are you going?" I whispered.

"None of your business," she said, "but if you have to know I am going to suck my boyfriend's dick in the back of his car." I wondered if that meant that she was a prostitute.

A policeman came to warn us against terrorists. His speech on letter bombs inaugurated our new lecture theatre. The room was radiant with fresh paint and the august responsibility to advance arts and culture on the proceeds of an Old Girl endowment. "This," explained the plainclothes officer with a home-made brown-bread accent, "is what a letter bomb look like." He held up an envelope with a hand-written address and no sender details. The girls sniggered. I felt a twinge of shame. I wanted to explain that Afrikaans verbs don't conjugate.

"How do we know it's a letter bomb before it explodes?" Camelia Clarke asked, hiding behind her long fringe. The colour of Peels Creamed Honey if you could buy it in a bottle. I wondered who invented the names on paint charts. Firebird. Sleepy Girl. Clotted Cream. I would not mind having that job one day, but I was going to be a doctor.

The policeman cleared his throat. It was not the kind of hostile environment his training had prepared him for. "You must never open a parcel from someone you don't know. Also, it can sometimes has a strange smell."

"More likely to be a Valentine's card from some idiot at Hilton, perfumed with disgusting deodorant," Camelia whispered with her hand to her mouth and her eyes to the floor. Mr Merriweather stood up and said, "Any questions?" The sergeant's parting gift was a public awareness chart with diagrams of bombs. Mr Merriweather stuck the poster on our classroom wall. *Ken jou vyand. Know your enemy.* It radiated the odour of collaboration.

"What a waste of time. These Dutchmen are such idiots, who would want to bomb us? I wish they would at least try to speak English properly." Olivia turned to me. "Not you, of course, Dominique, you are different. You aren't like the rest of them."

Camelia opened the music room door with fingers as delicate as climbing vines and a mind primed for mathematics. "We are going to the Natal Schools' Poetry Competition prize-giving tonight." She had a habit of looking away when she spoke, her voice trailing to a whisper mid sentence. "We leave in a quarter of an hour. At least we will be spared the horror of eating here for one night."

I ran down from the music block, put on my formal suit, a navy pencil skirt worn with a collared shirt and blazer, and searched for a satin ribbon. I had met Camelia's brother at a debating society meeting. I thought about him during the day. I thought about him at night. I thought about him while I practised my scales. John Clarke. Hair ribbons were compulsory on school outings. Failure to comply was punished by having to stand in the hall on bricks for an hour on Saturday mornings under the eyes of a prefect. Camelia was waiting in the bus and I sat next to her.

A voice from the back whispered, "I hear Paul is going to be there tonight, Dominique." Others giggled. "Who is asking him to the matric ball?" More tittering.

Camelia rolled her eyes and mouthed, "Birdbrains." The voices were familiar. I kept being summoned to the tickey box by anonymous callers, hearing only garbled whispers and the rhythmic solicitations of the coin slot. It seemed too breathtakingly childish that they would be phoning me only to hear Paul's sister's voice.

Paul called St Anne's "The Shire" because of the mist and the cottages and the hobbits. That's what he called our housemistresses. He was proud that Tolkien was born a Free Stater. The driver swung the bus onto the highway that sloped down a long hill into the humid soup of a Pietermaritzburg summer evening. Heavily laden articulated trucks careened past along the road flanked by arrestor beds. There was a joke that Indian families held picnics in arrestor beds. Or Afrikaans ones. We drove through slumbering suburbs, past the town hall celebrated for its many red bricks towards the university renowned for its drunken students.

Paul leant against a wall with his hands in his pockets. He gave me a slow smile. Camelia and I stood to the side while the matrics formed a cordon of fluttering hands and hitched skirts around him. They dispersed reluctantly into *Modern Languages* where ivy climbed the walls with sticky feet. It had the forlorn air of a building used by many but loved by none.

"This is my friend Camelia Clarke."

"Pretty birds of a feather." Paul gave her an appraising look. "You remember Adi," Paul said. "We were just talking about his visit to Dakar."

"Were you actually there?" I stammered.

"For Pete's sake, come inside," Mr Merriweather said, unlatching the sliding locks that kept the doors open. I wanted to ask Adi what it was like to be overseas. Whether they were scared of the security police. If he had seen a baobab tree. I had looked at old photographs of Senegal in a library book. Ma would have given anything to have been at that meeting. Pa once flew to England via Nairobi in a dud plane that needed repairs when they landed in Kenya. The Kenyans ferried the other passengers to hotels in the city while Pa and other white South Africans were kept in a stuffy room, not even given fresh air. Pa said we were the skunks of the world.

We went inside and sat in half moons according to school affiliation. Teachers threatened and pleaded in turn for silence. Camelia pointed across the lecture theatre to her brother. John was as tall and dark as she was small and blonde. He held my gaze under the hot fluorescent lights and fake leather seats and graffitied benches.

A woman with red lipstick and rolls of fat under her purple dress shuffled to the podium to announce the best collection of poems. "It is with special mention that we award this prize to Paul Botha from Hilton College," she said, shifting from one scuffed high heel to the other, "who shows such a precocious understanding of nascent sexuality. Such a poignant perspective on the irredeemably alienated state of the human soul." There were loud cheers from Hilton College. She pouted her painted lips and cleared her throat.

"It is a rare pleasure to see such dexterity in metaphor. Such promise."

Paul walked down to the podium in his blazer and tie. He kissed her proffered cheeks, balled his fist into the black power salute and then collapsed his arm, laughing. The half moons emptied into bedlam. I tried to reach Paul, but Mr Merriweather ordered us to the bus.

77

It was forbidden to show public affection, even to a sibling. I watched John leave.

The bus went haltingly up the hill sleeved in mist. Water song fell from the chapel's roof shingles onto the stone path. Hadedas craked on the lawn as I walked down to Mollie Stone alone. I asked Mrs Motherway if I could use the phone. She unlocked the door to the tickey box and smoked in the corridor as I told of Paul's triumph. Pa sounded awed. Ma said, "I expected no less."

I thought about John until I fell asleep. When I woke up. While I practised my scales.

Mrs Motherway called me into her annex. Calls to her private line were tolerated by grave exception. It was Ma. "Paul is in trouble, do you know about this?"

Ma's voice was in the high register of indignation. I wondered if they had caught him smoking or bunking. "They broke into the Old Boys' Club and drank everything in the clubhouse. The games master found them comatose on the cricket oval." I held the receiver from my ear as she shouted, "They are holding him responsible as ring-leader. He does not sound remotely remorseful."

Ma and Pa drove through the night. The next day they took me with them to Hilton. I did not want to go along. No-one spoke in the car. Paul was waiting outside Newnhams and Pa told him to get into the car.

"I know you are upset about your friend's death." Paul looked away as Pa spoke. "Sometimes fate exacts a terrible price, one that is hard to fathom. But one must not shame fate into returning. You know I lost a brother when I was a young man. One must be disciplined about misfortune."

A month earlier, Paul had helped to carry the coffin of his friend Nicolas Weeks in the driving rain through a cemetery over-looking the township where Casspirs trawled at night. The soil bled little red rivulets in the downpour while his parents stood together under an umbrella. Fragile, struck down, uncomprehending.

Paul stared out the window.

Pa opened the door. "They are considering making a criminal case against you boys for burglary."

"They will never do that Pa, the school is too obsessed with its precious reputation."

"Don't you talk back to me, Paul. You better apologise to the headmaster. They want to expel you. Do you understand me, sonny boy?" Pa was shouting and Paul looked down at his shoes. I could see a packet of cigarettes in his blazer pocket. "What's more, a man needs to hold his alcohol, drink responsibly. When you have earned the right to drink in the first place, for Christ's sake," Pa kept raging.

"You should be ashamed of yourself," Ma chimed in, "do you have any idea what it costs to be at this school?"

"Would it not be cheaper for you if they expelled me?" Paul asked.

"Don't think I'm not prepared to bliksem you, you hear me?" Pa turned around with his fist clenched. "You should take a leaf out of your sister's book."

"There is Mr Talbott now, we better go inside." I stayed in the car while Pa and Ma and Paul walked in different directions to the headmaster's office. The old leather seats in the Mercedes had a smoky smell that reminded me of Oupa's workshop. I pressed my face against the window. I wished I were at Wolwefontein.

After a long while, Paul came out of the office alone, got back into the car and slammed the door. "Self-righteous pedants. The truth is I am not sorry. If they are so in love with the supposed truth they should accept that. Drinking spirits kept under lock and key for some desperadoes who come round on Saturdays to get pissed and reminisce about school as the greatest time in their lives is not exactly a capital offence. Fuck them.

"I need a smoke," Paul said as we watched Ma and Pa walk towards the car. He looked at me and smiled. His eyes were red.

The verdict was rustication. Sent home in disgrace until further notice. I was jealous. The drive back to St Anne's happened in silence. I ran down to Mollie Stone and cried into my pillow until the bell rang for prep.

Mr Talbott sent a letter later that week. *We have decided to give Paul a second chance. He is such a talented young man with such potential. We believe that his exuberance will be tempered by responsibility. We are making him a prefect and look forward to welcoming him back to school next year.*

Mrs Motherway said Paul playing centre in the first rugby team explained everything.

The last day of term arrived like an answered prayer. A Zulu princess who was in my class ripped off her shirt and danced topless with the catering staff on the front lawn. The headmaster's face went puce. My skirt fell over my hipbones and I pinned it in place. I had to go to the sanatorium twice a week to be weighed. "More weight loss and you will be in serious trouble, girlie," the sanatorium sister warned.

Our departure was delayed because someone had parked a coil in Louise Gray's suitcase. The culprit had to be found. Mrs Motherway walked up and down the bus aisle fuming, "To treat the girl who is your Head of House in this way defies decency. I hardly know what to say, so shamed am I by this outrage." It was silent but for Louise snivelling in the front of the bus, where she had a seat reserved as Head of House. Tamara boasted to the whole dorm about squatting over Louise's opened suitcase and shitting on top of her neatly folded pyjamas. "Serves that uptight bitch right for ratting on me." Eventually Mrs Motherway gave up and sent us on our way.

The bus travelled for hours before refuelling in Harrismith. Pa met me at the airfield in his four-seater Piper Arrow, bought after enough good crops and years of hankering. Planes are always traded in dollars and Pa had paid before the Rubicon speech sent the rand downriver. A good hedge, he called it at the time. Ma was not convinced. Pa saw me and said, "Good God." He pointed at my protruding ribs. "What's this nonsense?"

He handed me the navigation map. Pa flew illegally because he could no longer bluff his way through a pilot medical test. His failing eyesight was the result of a freak accident. A friend had brought a sailing boat to Rietpan one Saturday afternoon ten years ago just after

Christiaan was born. A small fire was made to cook meat and Ma put blankets under the willows. The swollen pan lapped at nearby pylons. A misguided setting of the rudder sent the mast against the power lines and burnt holes through Pa and stopped his heart. For months he lay in hospital with seeping wounds and the doctor's daily prognosis, "This man should not be alive."

The accident left a milky fleece slowly clouding his irises. A specialist at Baragwanath was going to cut out the cataracts once Pa finished planting. He was the country's best eye surgeon working in a public hospital for black people, but he saw no distinction in the colour of his patients. "Can you believe the Persians were performing cataract operations thousands of years ago with blades made of jasper. Bloody amazing," Pa said as he ran through his pre-flight check. "Magnetos. On. Oil Pressure. Normal. And so on. Let's go."

We took off from the sandy airfield with gravel flying at angles below the undercarriage over a flock of startled guinea fowl. "Watch out for bogeys," he said. That meant birds. I held the contour map on my lap. It was covered in sepia lines like bracelets looped through a shared elevation. "You should be seeing a river down there," Pa said impatiently. I strained to find a correlation between the legend on my lap and the veld below smudged in similar silver slivers of roads, rivers and railways.

"Ag Jirre," Pa said, grabbing the map and holding it right up to his face. He fiddled with various flight instruments and put the plane on autopilot. "I am going to have a sleep now. If you see any other aircraft, wake me up." He winked at me, "I really am a jewel of a man." He was asleep within minutes. We flew above the clouds in an envelope-blue sky. It was cold, silent and empty. Mr Merriweather said beauty was over-described, there was nothing left to say. The aeroplane started jigging up and down.

"What's that?" I woke Pa in a panic.

"Clear air turbulence," Pa said, refreshed from his nap, and nonchalant. "Can you see the silos?"

"I am trying, Pa," I said, loosening the seatbelt to lean forward. Through the parting clouds I saw the water that lay in the body of my longing. Rietpan. Pa tilted the wings and we swung low over the house to announce our arrival. Pigeons peeled off the roof and Christiaan and Nadia ran out onto the lawn. Ma waved to us from the front door, pushing Boetie's pram to and fro. Pa banked over the gum windbreak and steered towards the landing strip he had staked out between mielie fields. Pa said any landing one can walk away from is a good landing. He taxied the plane into the shed where Goldberg waited to greet us. The workshop smelt of grease and diesel and dust. I wanted to go on my knees and kiss the floor. I ran home along the path littered with seringa blossoms, past Pa's hospice for broken implements where he laboured away the hours instead of managing the farm from a desk in the modern way as Ma pleaded.

Selina laid out tea under the willow tree with apple crumble and thick cream that came in Consol glass jars from Wolwefontein.

"You have to eat," Ma insisted. I was suddenly ravenous. I ate three helpings while Boetie and Firi sat on the lawn guarded by Nadia's Border Collie. Firi was Cardow's son, and his mother Evelina was helping with all the extra washing. Cloth nappies hung in rows on the washing line and stewed in Milton's softener in buckets in the laundry. Paul said the puppy looked like a black and white Hilton College blazer. The name stuck. Hilton was a birthday present for Nadia. Paul said Pa had softened in his dotage. Paul worked hard in the workshop for the privilege of saying anything at all.

The days went too quickly. I memorised every room, every tree, the anonymous finches, the extravagant water birds, Christiaan's room with *Star Wars* stickers, Selina's rare smile, Pa's constant quest to swat flies. I never wanted to leave again.

Abel and Mary had retired to the township outside Klerksdorp and Abel had bought a second-hand Mercedes with his savings that he drove at sixty kilometres an hour. They never got sent off to a homeland in the end. Maureen got her doctorate and a job in Chicago. 'er letters were still filled with longing. Elsabe was away on a Voor-
'ker camp when I phoned and her mother said she would pass on
'ssage.

I helped Selina make sugared peanuts for us to take back to school. The nuts came from the field next to the house. Christiaan and I split the papery pods to harvest the twin kernels. Selina roasted them in canola oil while sugar syrup slowly boiled on the stove. She added a few drops of Robertsons' Berry Pink to tinge the crusts.

There had been talk of political unrest erupting in the townships. Some of the parents felt it might be unsafe to let the buses travel. On the drive Pa had told us about a feared North African wind that blows the Sahara across the Mediterranean covering Southern Europe in ochre dust. Ma looked out the window and mouthed, "Blah blah blah."

"Moordwinde," he went on. "They are like our August winds. The season of civil unrest, family murders and suicide. That's when the real political trouble will start. Not now."

I lay my head against the window praying for unseasonal political unrest.

"But," he said, "you must remember that those are also the winds that bring the rain."

Paul was driving with a learner's licence. He had earned forgiveness by becoming a prefect. Pa kept making comments about his driving in English. "Give the child a chance, Andries," Ma said from the back. Pa and Ma's English suddenly sounded strange to me. It fell into the category that at school would be considered awful. I felt ashamed for thinking it.

Paul eventually pulled off the side of the road and said, "Why don't you just drive then, Pa?"

Pa got into the driver's seat, slammed the door and we sped off to the farm Middenspruit where the famous poet lived. Wolwefontein lay four farms beyond along the False River. Ma had arranged to take Paul to her on our way back to school. I could not believe Ma was so presumptuous. She came out to greet us, her face welcoming and curious.

Pa gestured towards Paul and Ma, "This lot are finishing me off." He sighed and sat down on the ball-and-claw armchair, sinking into the worn cushions. Ma sat on the chair furthest from Pa.

"Enjoy the view, I'll send out some tea." The poet smiled at Paul and led the way into the house. Paul followed her with his typed folios. I walked down the lawn and sat under a white stinkwood that overlooked the river's brittle banks. It was wider here than at Wolwefontein because of the weir at the Geldenhuys boundary. A yearly tithe of calving mud widened the river's path and she exacted it in summer.

I watched hoopoes foraging on the mown lawn. Two gums held a poplar pole between them in opposing clefts. There were trees like this on all the farms. Hide was run by singing workers along the poplar's abrasive grain until the skin transformed into leather. Rieme were used for tying and harnessing before the advent of rope. Rieme also served as the tongues for whips, thinning to a forked point.

On the opposite bank a spooked korhaan flew in widening circles around her nest. I cleaned wet mud off the sole of my school shoe with a porcupine quill. Old Vytjie from Wolwefontein said the river was a giant snake that grew fat in summer and moulted in winter. On the banks lay the cracked mud scales of shucked skin. Water returned in spring, convening across a sagging relief of coursing water.

On the stoep there was the civil clinking of teaspoons but no conversation. I lay down on the cool clover that grew in the shade. I thought Paul was very brave. I would not be able to speak if she asked me a question. I had almost fallen asleep when I heard my name called.

"We are going now," Pa said, climbing into the car. I sat in the back with Ma and the writer came to the open window. "There really is something here, Sandra," she whispered to Ma. Her fingers clutched Paul's typed folio. I sat quietly, in awe. Pa winked at me in the rearview mirror and said, "Jy vang vlieë." I closed my mouth.

"Never forget, Paul," Antjie called as we drove away, "a writer writes."

CHAPTER 7

Boarding school improved along with my accent. I took elocution lessons from an old spinster who lived on the grounds in a cottage shawled in flowers. Black-eyed Susans lolled on the gateposts and jasmine spilt across the trellis as spry and fragrant as Miss Kniep. I saw her once a week before dinner when she emerged at precisely six o'clock, walking always as if on stage.

"Time, dear," she would call, flouncing the billowy sleeves of her silk blouse. Miss Kniep believed the cadence of proper English lay in the five-footed verse of consumptive poets.

Thou still unravished bride of quietness
Thou foster child of silence and slow time

There was talk in the common rooms as to whether Miss Kniep was still unravished, whether she had suffered a fate worse than death. The word *Miss* stood like a mirror in front of her surname, its four letters cobwebbed in a private history too delicate for scrutiny, I thought. The Royal College of London sent a posh man from Manchester once a year to grade her Speech and Drama students. My talk was on the origin of Indo-European languages. Miss Kniep found reference to the Germanic provenance of English distasteful and hurried me along. "Remember though, dear, to speak slowly and clearly to the examiner." She was joining him for dinner in the Tudor dining hall of the village hotel. "I do hope he's not dreary," Miss Kniep said, adjusting her freshly hennaed hair and pearl choker in turn. In her small kitchen a silver strainer held the dregs of the Earl Grey she drank with sugar and three drops of cream.

I shook as I delivered my speech while the examiner twiddled a pencil in the cavernous school hall. Tap, tap, tap it went on the gleaming desk as he flinched at my flattened vowels. After the exam, I dawdled to the chapel. Mrs Merriweather wanted me to play the organ for the Christmas concert so that she could free up her hands to conduct the choir. She had the fretting quality of a squirrel, was married to the smiley-faced English teacher Mr Merriweather and they were as sunny as their surname. An organ is half flute, half furniture. I did not know how to play it properly with all the stops and pedals and pipes.

I sat in the choir loft with my hands on my lap. Jesus died and Mary wept in lancet windows colouring the nave. Votive candles shone in the chancel. At the foot of the holiest of holies, tapestry covered the communion bench.

In Ma's day it caused a scandal in Koppies when she refused to be confirmed. The NG church declined to marry Ma and Pa. Confirmation mattered less now. I wondered whether to bother. According to our school chaplain there might be lost opportunities for girls who aspired to leadership positions.

I took Elsabe's letter from my blazer pocket. Mail was pinned like butterflies behind a lattice of ribbons next to the headmaster's office. She wrote that Mr Kruger sometimes caned the high school boys till they bled. She wanted to study at university. There were four daughters and not enough money. I missed her, the dark house full of hunting trophies, even their albino pit bull with skin cancer. I pummelled the required carols over moaning keys before I walked back to Mollie Stone past the tennis courts where balls thudded rhythmically and scores were often disputed. Precious was carrying pots and a tray of custard slices for afternoon tea. On my pillow I found three handwritten messages with many exclamation marks. *Phone Paul urgently!!!!* I dialled the tickey box at Newnhams and he answered before it rang.

"Thank God. What took you so long?"

"I was in the chapel. I only have one ten cent coin."

"I have my Afrikaans literature oral tomorrow and I have not read any novels."

"That's terrible Paul." The phone died. He called back immediately.

"Don't be sanctimonious. Just give me a synopsis of three books and what you thought of them."

"It won't work."

"I can assure you it's often preferable not to read a book in order to form a proper opinion. I don't have enough coins for an argument."

I sighed. "Do you have pen and paper?"

"I do. Shoot."

I scratched in my memory for plot and character inside the tiny booth with yellow floors overlooking the forest. I had shed many homesick tears in that room with the charges reversed to Ma and Pa. I heard his pencil scribbling my inadequate recollections onto paper. "Good luck Paul. You will need it."

The phone gobbled his last coin and the line went dead.

The whole school gathered in the chapel to rehearse for the Christmas Concert. Mrs Merriweather winced at the descant's involuntary key change and my faulty footwork. In the middle of "Hark, the Herald Angel Sings" Mr Merriwether called me down from the choir loft, his round face ashen with no trace of the spilling smile.

"We are so disappointed," he said, shaking his head and walking out onto the veranda overlooking the front lawn. Paul was naked and peeing into the memorial fountain singing loudly and out of tune. When Mr MacAdam walked towards him he jumped out and ran around in circles. "Hey, old Danny Boy, you wanna play catchers?" Paul laughed.

I looked up at Mr Merriwether. "Can I go back to the organ now?"

"Such a good rugby player. I did not expect this of him."

The rehearsal had to be cancelled. The herald angels sang of Hilton boys. I picked up my sheet music and went down to Mollie Stone to avoid interrogation. I sat on my bed in the empty dormitory. I was angry with Paul for being so rude to Mr MacAdam. I knew the boys went drinking when they finished their final exams. It was part of tradition. Much vaunted and valourised tradition. I felt tired all the time. I lay in my bed, overwhelmed by weariness that held me by the ankles. For weeks every step had felt like it was taken through sinking sand.

"Where is Mrs Motherfuck? I want to have a word with Mrs Motherfuck." It was Paul's voice shouting loudly down the corridor that led to Mrs Motherway's rooms. I ran into the passage.

"Are you mad!" I pushed him into my room. "Get into my cupboard. Where are your clothes?"

"Sister, you are so sweet. My Number Ones are just below this little Victorian grotesquery ... this jail for privileged virgins ... this birdcage for songbirds."

"You're drunk. Stop talking shit and tell me where your clothes are."

"No need to be uncouth."

"Mrs Motherway will call the police."

"I am not worried about jail. The worthwhile writers have all spent time inside. I would consider it part of my literary training."

I found his suit in a heap by the dustbins. I ran back and made him dress, standing against the door to keep it shut.

"Anyway," he said, "they have called the police already. I heard sirens when that geriatric pervert chased us round the front lawn."

"You mean the headmaster? Oh God, you have to get out of here."

Mollie Stone was right on the edge of the school grounds bordering a quiet plantation of pines. I helped him through a break in the fence.

"I'll be back," he slurred and then fell over a log.

"Promise me you won't." I was almost in tears.

"Stop panicking. I'm out of here. For ever. By the way, I got an A for my oral. At least this expensive private school education is not being wasted on you."

Through the rush of the concert and packing and farewells I saw our car in the parking lot, the lone Free State registration plate sandblasted along dirt roads. "Freedom from the tyranny of the bell," Fiona said. She was coming home with me. Her parents fastened frail hopes for improved marks on the fantasy of an Afrikaans farm holiday. Goldberg wore his Sunday suit, an unconvincing scowl and the grave demeanour of a newly appointed chauffeur.

Paul had hitchhiked back to the farm and arrived there in the middle of the night. "The kleinbaas did wrong." Paul sometimes called Goldberg an unctuous Pharisee.

When we stopped for petrol and restrooms, he polished the steering wheel with a shammy cloth. There were no facilities for him and he walked into the veld behind the garage. Goldberg drove extremely slowly and did not overtake a single car. Fiona and I giggled in the back seat, taking turns to beg him to drive faster. With every request, he slowed down more. He looked at me in the rear-view mirror and smiled. "It's my birthday Dommie, you mustn't forget," he said. I baked him a birthday cake every year. He liked the vinnige sjokolade-laagkoek recipe in *Kook en Geniet* with hundreds and thousands and chocolate icing.

I was hoping Ma and Pa would not still be angry with Paul when we got home. I imagined the fire in the sitting room and everyone waiting for us. I had spent the previous weekend with Camelia in Durban and her brother had kissed me in the living room while Camelia's mother took her to the orthodontist. It was my first kiss. I was waiting to tell Fiona.

"Welcome, welcome, welcome." Pa insisted on taking Fiona by the arm and showing her to what he called "your quarters" with theatrical courtesy.

"I hope there aren't any snakes here. Or spiders?" Fiona asked.

"Of course there are snakes," I laughed. In Natal rain spiders the size of pigeons shuffled along cornices hunting for geckos before oncoming storms. In foliage their nests hung spun like candyfloss around branch ends. Here we mainly fished harmless daddy-longlegs out of the bath. When we were little, we worried about the button spider as well as whirlpools, sinking sand and tidal waves. The butcher in town knew somebody in Klerksdorp whose cousin died horribly of a necrotic hand after turning over a rock in his back garden. By the seaside Christiaan and I used to take turns on the lookout for a thick black line on the horizon that might augur a tsunami.

After dinner we sat in the sitting room and drank tea. Ma and Pa were going to Cape Town for a week to attend a political conference. "Our political views have marginalised us from playing a role in our community," Pa explained at length to Fiona, stoking the fire with a brass shovel. "No Afrikaans person from Viljoenskroon invites us to their homes any more. Except for Johan and Sonja Geldenhuys, and for their solidarity I am deeply grateful." Fiona looked bored.

"My grandfather was a member of parliament in the Free State Republic. His constituency was made up of eighty voters in the Bothaville district. Men only, of course." The Hansard records of the Volksraad were mouldering in forgotten Dutch in bound copies in the sunroom. "This was his chair in the Volksraad." He made Fiona read the embossed silver plaque screwed into the ebony frame of the red leather chair that was only for show and not use.

Paul Michiel Botha. Oranje-Vrijstaat Volksraad. 1888–1895.

"He is the namesake of that obstreperous shit over there," Pa said pointing at Paul.

Paul stared into the fire. Ma was taking Nadia and Boetie along to Cape Town. Christiaan was going to spend the week with a friend in town. Every afternoon he hit a ball against the garage wall for hours and hours and never spoke unless he had to. Christiaan's silence drove Ma to distraction.

A woman came from Johannesburg early the next morning to drive to Cape Town with Ma and Pa. There were stickers on her car that read *Apartheid Free Zone* and *Equal rights for gays and lesbians Now!* Paul traced an arrow towards the label inserting the phrase *Let's* HOMO*genise Now!* in a font of parted dust.

We waved goodbye. She leaned out the car window and said, "Dominique and Paul, what a wonderful example you are to your younger siblings."

As the car went clunking over the cattle grid, Paul went to the storeroom and carried a box of liquor to his room. He poured a whiskey for himself and Fiona. He looked up at me, "What's wrong, Miss Priss? Why should Ma and Pa be the only ones having some fun?" Paul said Ma and Pa were going to Cape Town for tea and cakes and fiddles playing to the tune of Rome burning. Die Demokratiese Partytjie, he called it.

"Pa left the key for the storeroom in case you need access to the guns."

"That is a joke. The only weapon in there is Oom Boxer's decorative blunderbuss. The only thing of interest in the gun cabinet is Pa's whiskey. He should have thought about that."

"Who is Oom Boxer?" Fiona asked.

"Pa's uncle who only wore a top hat and tails, never worked a day in his life and always used to say 'thank God today is Sunday, so that I may also get some rest'."

Fiona kicked off her sandals and sat next to Paul. He pulled her closer and lit up a cigarette.

"When Oom Boxer inherited the original family farm Uitsig, he sold up immediately and drifted through Europe on the proceeds for seven years. He came back penniless and Pa had to vacate his room so that Oom Boxer could lie there and die slowly from delirium tremens." Paul laughed. "Apparently he used to beg the maid to buy liquor from the smous, which he then kept under his bed. She did because then he used to shit himself less. Still in top hat and tails."

There was a knock on the door. September stood there, cap in hand. "Kleinbaas, the cattle are out. I need the kleinbaas to come and help."

"Bugger," Paul said getting up.

"He'll probably be a while," I said to Fiona.

"I'll just wait," she smiled.

I lay back and listened to the dawn chorus and the willow rustling against my window. I would not have to go back to Natal for six weeks. Abundance. Joy. Fiona came into my room and sat on my bed. We burst out laughing. I told her about John. How much I liked him. She said she was bored with being a virgin.

I was baking for the tuisnywerheid to make some pocket money during the holiday. I made Cornish pasties with vegetables from the garden cubed into mince filling.

"The blacks buy them," Tannie Suzette had told me. She ran the tuisnywerheid. "You know, my child, if it was not for them, our little shop would not stay afloat for much longer." Tannie Suzette made the best koeksisters in the district. We all bought them. The blacks. The whites. Even the Lebanese. Ma said you could eat off the floor in any Lebanese household in town. Tannie Suzette's standards had to be excellent to be considered good enough.

"You are quite the boeremeisie," Fiona said when we fetched more eggs from the coop. She stood in her suede slippers picking feathers off the shells.

I mixed the batter for Goldberg's birthday cake. "We can take it to the stat once it has cooled and the icing is done."

Fiona sat at the kitchen table dunking a koeksister into her tea. "Who does your mother like to hang out with here in the bundus?" she asked, licking the sweet syrup off her fingers. Paul came into the kitchen looking for the bakkie keys. Fiona blushed when she saw him.

"Where are you going? The shops are all closed."

It was the 16th of December. Dingaan's Day. Last year the Griesels complained to the police that Pa's tractors were working in the fields on this sacred day of commemoration. Pa shouted at the constable, "Tell that hypocrite he can go to hell."

"I am going to see Vusi." Paul winked at me. "Coming?" he said to Fiona. Pa warned Paul before he left about driving without a licensed driver in the car. Goldberg had to accompany him at all times. An accident could lead to manslaughter charges. Fiona got up and followed him out the door.

I took the last tray out of the oven and went to my room to practise piano. I had promised Mrs Merriweather I would prepare for my exam. I played all my scales in legato and staccato over four octaves in hypnotic repetition until Paul burst into the room shouting, "Don't you know another fucking tune?" His eyes were bloodshot. Fiona stood behind him with eyes equally red. "What's wrong?" I asked. "Have you been crying?"

They giggled. "You need to chill out sister. Come and smoke a spliff. I've made a hotbox out of the shower."

"No thank you," I gasped and stormed past them.

I ran down into the garden and climbed up the ladder to Nadia's tree house. Pa had built it for her in the biggest willow overlooking the dam. Dagga. I could not believe Fiona. The horses under the gums trotted closer. The mare pushed her snout against the fence imploringly. We sometimes fed the horses sugar when Pa was not looking. According to him it was no treat for an animal to have rotten teeth.

I went back to the house and into the pantry and saw all but one of the Cornish pasties left on the tray. There were honey trails across the table, dirty knives on the floor and bread stuck in the toaster turning to charcoal. Paul came downstairs smiling.

"I can't believe you made this mess," I said. "Who the hell do you think should clean up after you?"

"We had the munchies. It looks like you are doing a good job."

"Could you stop being so self-indulgent for a second and help me, perhaps?" I shouted.

"Could you stop acting so fucking holier-than-thou for a second and try to enjoy yourself instead?" he screamed.

I sat down on the floor and started crying. "We are going to get into serious trouble. Pa is going to figure out you've been drinking the whiskey. If you go into the township again to buy dagga, the police are going to catch you. There are security police all over the place." He sat down next to me.

"You won't get into serious trouble. I'll just pour in some cheap crap to fill up the bottles. Pa won't know the difference."

He moved closer. "As for the security police, those fascists are too fucking scared to go into the township at night and too stupid to catch me. Vusi's looking out for me."

He put his arm around my shoulders. "Their so-called impimpi is my dealer. So stop worrying about it. I am sorry about your pies, though."

I rammed my elbow into his ribs as hard as I could. "Sometimes you can be a real arsehole."

"I don't necessarily disagree with you." He laughed, getting up off the floor and lending me a hand.

Paul's matric results arrived the next morning by post. He had distinctions in maths, English and Afrikaans and phoned the hotel in Cape Town to tell Ma and Pa. "I can't believe Ma," he fumed. "Only got A's for the subjects I didn't need to study for, she said. Fuck that, I got the university exemption Ma and Pa expected. Let's celebrate."

Paul spent the afternoon rigging the raft. Fiona baked dagga cookies and I filled a flask of Milo and brandy as Paul instructed. The whiskey had run out and Fiona guessed the ratio of brandy to milk. We packed citronella candles and Pa's binoculars. One could see the pockmarks on the moon with them.

Paul pushed the raft out of the shallows with a long punting pole. The black water curled and whispered around the pontoons. Coots and moorhens scattered briefly and then settled. A full moon floated slowly starwards behind the blue gums. We drifted to the middle of the dam and Paul threw out the anchor. He rolled a joint and passed it to Fiona. I drank from the flask, heaving at the taste of burnt grapes.

Fiona dangled her legs in the water, smoking a cigarette.

I took off my clothes and slipped into the water off the back of the raft. Fiona stood up. "Aren't there creatures in there?" she asked, dipping her foot into the water. Paul walked up behind her and gently pushed her. She came up laughing and swam towards me.

"Here's to Cape Town," Paul said, stripping off his clothes and taking a deep swig from the flask.

"Here's to what in Cape Town?" I asked him as he swam towards us in the moonlight.

"Here's to supporting sanity. To getting stoned."

Fiona pulled me towards her and we kissed. I pushed them away, laughing, and climbed back onto the raft. The fecund smell of summer clung to fine mats of water grass ladled onto the pontoons. Occasionally a barbel broke the surface. Drumming came from the stat. During the last few years we hardly ever heard it any more.

I lit the lanterns. Fiona stood naked on the edge of the raft slowly drying herself with our shared towel. Paul picked up Nadia's ukulele and held it out to me.

"I don't know how to play that thing."

"Please Sliminique. Play my favourite Jaap Fischer song. You said yourself it's just two chords." He passed the flask to me.

I took a deep gulp and found something that approximated the A chord. Then E. Then A again. Paul sat next to me and Fiona lay down beside him. We looked up at the beckoning flares of the Southern Cross. "Don't stop," Paul said. We both knew the words.

Omdat ik van je houd
Omdat ik van je houd
Krijg ik het zo ontzettend koud
Als jij niet bij mij bent

En ik kan wel een dans met een ander doen
Maar toch blijf ik denken aan je zoen
Dus kan ik het beter maar nooit meer doen
Omdat ik van je houd

From far away we saw a car turn off the main road and onto the farm. Paul leapt up. "Oh fuck, where's the punting pole?" We stumbled round the raft in the darkness, laughing. Paul said, "We'll just pull up the anchor. Luckily the prevailing wind is in the direction of home."

We drifted to the edge of the pan and Paul jumped off to pull the raft into mooring. Ma and Pa were standing at the bottom of the lawn waiting for us. Pa held Ma by her heaving shoulders.

Vusi Dlamini was lying dead in the morgue. Knifed through the heart.

"Tell your father he shouldn't go and hide behind that kaffir's death. Your milk cows are in my lucerne lands."

"Oom, the volk have all gone to the funeral."

"Tell him today is the day when I shoot his entire herd. Understand me clearly, girlie."

He slammed the phone down. Oom Jan Southwell. The black people called him Soutvoet.

I told Pa when he came to the house.

"To think I am the only person in the district still speaking to that bloody miserable old shit," Pa said. He took out his hanky and spat phlegm into it, then folded it away into his shirt pocket.

"Ou Soutvoet. I have helped him harvest when no worker was prepared to set foot on that farm. Just last week I saw Tant Lizzie in town with dark glasses. Then you must know, that piece of garbage is hitting her again." Ma was sitting in front of her dressing table putting in her lenses. "Ek's sommer lus en stuur vir Paul oor Vlakpan toe om vir Oom Jan te gaan donner," Pa continued.

"Where is Paul?" Ma asked. Martha came in with tea. She was no longer shy or thin like when she first came looking for work. She wore Ma's second-hand skirt and a tweed jacket over a self-embroidered T-shirt covered in butterflies. Her in-laws had taken everything, even her clothes. A Sotho widow had no rights. It made Ma mad.

She put the tray on a mahogany table facing the view across the pan.

"I sent him with Abram to select some animals."

We sold a lot of our cattle for funerals. For cash. Even though Pa said he always gave unto Caesar what was due unto Caesar. Rietpan was close enough to town for the mourners to walk the sacrificial cow back to Rammulotsi. Pa would not let the Dlaminis pay. Ma complained that Pa kept making exceptions like that. As a result, we failed to flourish like some other farmers.

"If there is one decent custom of us Afrikaners it is that we always help each other through difficult times. Like with my brother Paul's funeral. The Snymans came to harvest the crop, we did not have to do a thing that year," Pa said angrily. "Soutvoet is a real turd."

Ma mouthed the words "a solvent turd" into the mirror.

"Maureen wants to read Paul's poem about the Northern Free State at the funeral. She said Paul's words reminded her of home when she was in America. Is that not touching?" Ma covered her face with her hands. She said we would be able to close the door on Vusi's death, but it will blow a draught through the rest of Abel and Mary's lives.

Ma and Pa had gone to Abel and Mary's door with the news. Mary wanted their pastor with them before they went to identify Vusi at the morgue. Pa and Ma drove them into the township in the middle of the night to fetch their priest. Ma was sobbing, "When they pulled the sheet back all Mary said was 'Vusi!'"

Pa looked at Ma then turned to me.

"Pour me some tea."

I got up from their brass bed and took the cosy off the pewter pot.

"For God's sake, Dominique, wait for it to brew."

I heard Paul's footsteps down the hall. He stood in the doorway holding an envelope full of notes and put the money down on the table next to Pa's hat.

"I presume you've counted it," Pa said, taking the envelope off the table. He turned to me. "What are you waiting for, pour."

I placed the cups onto the saucers and put the requisite one-and-a-quarter teaspoon of sugar into Pa's tea.

Paul turned to Ma and asked if he could borrow Oupa Boetie's suit for the funeral.

"You will have to ask your father."

Pa stirred the teaspoon clinking against the china.

Ma sighed, "It's hanging in your father's cupboard. Take the moth-balls out of the pockets."

Pa looked at Paul and me. "Go and get dressed. I don't want to be late."

I put on flesh-coloured stockings and a dress hemmed below the knee. Ouma Celia gave it to me because she said I was nice and thin. I went to the garage and sat in the back of the old Mercedes. A silk moth as large as a child's hand clung to the wall with a startled eye on each wing. It had been there since the day before without moving at all. Martha climbed in and sat next to me. She put Boetie on my lap and held Firi on hers. Firi's mother Evelina was in the township cooking the funeral meal. Boetie and Firi had become inseperable. Pa called them Vinkel and Koljander. "Where is the firstborn?" Martha asked. She disapproved when Pa and Ma were cross with Paul. "He's probably hiding from the baas," I said. We both smiled. Ma and Pa got into the car. Christiaan and Paul followed in the bakkie with mourners in the back. We drove along the avenue of honey locusts that led to the tarred road with pods and leaves and doves rustling as Ma had prom-ised all those years ago when the trees were planted. Heat corrugated the horizon towards Rammulotsi. Women in frilly-collared blouses and red jackets with clasped Bibles made way for us on the dusty road. No church in the township was big enough. The service was taking place at the high school.

There were people everywhere. Mourners had come on foot from the farms, in taxis from neighbouring towns and on the overnight bus from QwaQwa. The hall was packed. Pa said when a young person dies, the funeral is always big. Men were shaking hands and greeting in subdued voices as we walked towards the hall. Maureen was sitting with her head bowed next to the coffin. Pa turned around to us and muttered, "You children, don't for God's sake come inside. I don't want some old person making way for you."

There was a lone peach tree casting mottled shade in the lee of the hall. Paul walked towards the tree and Christiaan and I followed him. A few boys were leaning against the trunk. They wordlessly made space for us in the shade. I looked up at the overhang of pitted branches. The tree gave all its vigour to the peaches. Tatty leaves hung like afterthoughts. A red-headed finch was pecking at fallen fruit. The service began with a hymn. Loss stung the air.

Paul gently poked me in the ribs with his elbow and pointed. Two police vehicles were patrolling the fence. The sound of the engines drowned in rising song. When the singing died down, Maureen stood up. We watched her through the open hall doors, her voice thin and wavering. "My brothers and sisters. I am going to read about this place. Where we all come back to." Paul sat with his head in his hands looking at his shoes.

"Northern Free State, July 1987," she said, drying her eyes, "Morena."

come with me
to the bareback veld

along numb horizons the wind has
blown for days blown
blackening the trees between

emptying mielie fields geese are
breaking white beating
a laboured flight
into the wind the blue the thin skeletal sing
of distant telephone wires
across chill blue horizons
rest the windsculpted thighs
neck palms of cloud
encupping a shy christfire
the once icebright sun smoothed
in the subtle wash of the wind
the wind will always draw
the substance from the sky slow flowing
erode the landscape into obscurity numbing
horizons as it combs the sand
across my huddled landscape:

come
come with me
to the bareback veld
where the wind will
distilling, blow
you into me
me into you

Maureen walked towards Ma and fell into her arms. The pastor began his fervent benediction. Paul patted his blazer pockets for cigarettes. The patrol vehicle idled in front of the gates with a view of us sitting under the tree. Paul lit his cigarette and gestured his middle finger at them. "Fucking boere." There was a rustle of laughter under the tree. He handed cigarettes round. After the service, Paul was going to Cape Town University on a train with his Paul Botha the 6th satchel filled with empty lined notebooks. He said he was going there to launch his career as a human being.

I saw Leon van Jaarsveld in the police van. He used to pass down soliciting notes to me in primary school, written on powder-blue paper covered in stickers, filled with banalities about wind and love. I still kept them in my drawer. *So waai die wind, so waai die gras, so waai my liefde teen jou vas.*

CHAPTER 8

The August winds blew past calendar boundaries across September into October. The rains are late. Pa must wait for the first downpour before rippers are sent in to turn the soil. A spare place setting at lunch awaits experts who might arrive to pronounce on the fertility of sand. Soil husbandry is discussed over coffee and cigarettes. Its composition, its allies and its enemies. White goosefoot, spindlepod, pretty lady, apple of Peru, cocklebur. All florid opportunists colonising the land and sitting tight in the corrosive wind, their leaves thin and impervious.

Martha draws the curtains to keep out the dust, but it finds a way. Windmills roll and tilt. Aquifers run dry. During the day Pa dismantles implements and oils dry rollerbearings. At dusk he stands with his hands across his chest contemplating the western horizon. Assessing clouds. The storms that skirt our land feel like a personal slight. I long to hear the rain on the tin roof. I make pacts with God about how much and when. The first downpour must be soft and persistent otherwise topsoil is pulled away in sheets of diminishing return. Too little rain, then saplings wither. So we wait.

Our apricot tree grows impatient and blossoms, the branches threaded with a delicate clotting of cherries in milk. Ma cut some flowering boughs and put them a vase, like a Japanese drawing.

Oupa Bob and Ouma Celia came down from Pretoria so that Oupa could help at the welding machine in Pa's sombre workshop. They brought watermelons from the Lowveld and Ma carved the sweet flesh with an ice-cream scoop into round balls to serve for dessert. Ma was fighting the drought from her kitchen.

Paul had not been to the farm all year. He failed the only midyear exam he attempted, writing *SUPPRESS SHAKESPEARE* across the English literature paper. He managed to convince the university to give him a second chance. He wrote a long letter to Ma and Pa saying how sorry he was and that he would not disappoint them again. Ma wrote back that his actions reflected on us all. That he came from an honourable family. That he must respect the fact that he is part of us, and that we are part of him.

I had not been at school since the beginning of the year. Ma took me from doctor to doctor, even the specialists were confounded. I had wilted like one of Pa's saplings. In the beginning I did all the work sent from school, now I mostly shadowed Martha around the kitchen. I felt ashamed. My illness was suspect, unlike the stroke that had lain Ouma Koeks low on her bed as an act of God. Pa said I had nothing to be ashamed of.

The widows who brooded over Ouma Koeks in her death vigil always arrived in time for meals and gloomy pronouncements. Strange things were happening. A lightning strike had dislodged the giant praying hands of cement off the pedestal in the Apostolic churchyard. A sign. There were mutterings of die Siener and die Apokalips and the Illuminati. The top strand of barbed-wire fencing on the borders of the farm was rolled up over night and carried away. Fertiliser disappeared from the store. Tannie Mara would tuck in her napkin and grumble, "In the old days we could teach the kaffirs a thing or two, but not any more." Ma said these widows were carrion feeders but she made them tea and pretended to listen. Selina was caught with milk and cream and doilies in her bag. Ma had to let her go. The principle of it, she said. Now Selina tends her yard at the stat and always waves when we drive past.

Martha and I stood in the kitchen while Ma gave instructions on making watermelon jam before they left for town. Ouma Celia was going with to fetch the post and some groceries. I had cut the rind into squares, discarded the green skin into the chicken swill and laid it in slaked lime overnight.

Ma showed Martha the Consol glass jars in the pantry. "It is important to sterilise the jars with boiling water, otherwise bacteria blooms in the potted jam and it has to be thrown away. Cut the watermelon into smaller squares and prick them with a fork. Holes allow the syrup to soak in. Boil the fruits until they turn tender. Only then do you make the syrup with three cups of sugar, enough water, some lemon juice and bruised ginger."

Ma opened Ouma Koeks's recipe book while Ouma Koeks lay upstairs in an unremitting sleep. Ouma Celia walked in on high heels clicking on the polished tiles, holding Spokie under her arm. Ma rolled her eyes when she saw the dog. Spokie was Ouma's only surviving prisoner of love, labouring away her last days on a silk cushion. "We won't be long." Ma waved and Ouma followed her.

We no longer had our own dog. Hilton had died from nervous exhaustion and we had buried him in the garden under a Vaderland-swilg. Boetie threw himself crying into the dog's grave and Pa screamed at him to have some self-respect. After Hilton died, Pa started locking the doors at night. He took out the antique gun from the safe. As a further precaution Ouma Koeks's ancient Labrador, Pinky, laboured as watchdog under layers of indolence and collar fat. Ou Piet was employed as watchman and passed out in the middle of the workshop yard every night, unconscious but at his post. Pa just shrugged his shoulders and said, "As drunk as a fowl."

Making syrup is tricky because sugar turns moody as it melts. Martha watched me while she kneaded the rusk dough. Fresh ginger was hard to come by and the grocer from Madeira Fruiterers in town got it for Ma specially. To test the consistency, I poured a teaspoon of syrup onto a milk muslin. If it sank into the weft it was too runny. If it congealed into small balls it was ready. I folded the watermelon pieces into the pot evenly, dispersing the fruits according to the sloping cursives of Ouma's recipe. When the opaque squares grew clear, the cooled jam was decanted and sealed with wax. I fixed the lids with rice-paper bonnets and string. I used one of Ma's precious Royal Albert saucers that she received as a wedding gift to trace circles into the brittle sheets. Pa liked to eat the preserve without bread or butter. He always selected two squares from the jar and ate them with a knife and fork. Then he would press a napkin against his mouth and say, "One could not find a better dessert in any gourmet restaurant."

Martha patted the kneaded dough into a ball and lowered it into an oiled mixing bowl. She wrapped a patched eiderdown around the dish and placed it on the windowsill to rise. A goose feather peeked from a hole in the paisley silk. Paul loved the tall slices of sweet bread that she leavened with potato yeast.

Martha went outside to have her tea. I turned the pages of Ouma's handwritten recipe book that Ma called an heirloom and kept in the bookcase in the sitting room. I pried open the dog-eared pages stained with fat and flour. Paul had covered a page in his hard-wrought left-handed font with variations of a signature. PMB. Paul Michiel Botha. Paul M. Botha the 6th. I did the same thing on pieces of paper instead of doing my history project. On another page was a poem with the title and date neatly written and underlined. "Love poem for a winter's morning". 1986. He was sixteen when he wrote it.

> *unfolds this*
> *winter morning*
>> *blade clear,*
>>> *against which a soft*
> *shoulder of snowbirds:*
>
> *in a dry country*
> *the sun will*
> *unskin the land*
>
> *but here*
> *where we lie*
> *throat against*
> *throat,*
> *(along the handbridge between us)*
> *unfolds*
> *an absence of knives*

I allowed myself one thought about John after each folding of the watermelon syrup. I turned his words over and over until they had the right consistency. They always curdled. Ma wanted to know if he was my boyfriend. The last time I saw him, he took me to his room, locked the door and pulled the striped curtains closed. I sat perfectly still in the moth-coloured light of the late afternoon. He unbuttoned my blouse and lay me down on his bed. His mother was downstairs in her office marking first-year papers on economic theory. He ran his fingers along my arms and into my hands. The erythrina outside his bedroom window knocked against the glass. It was in flower. They call it a coral tree in Natal.

I wondered who Paul was in love with then, when he wrote the poem. I was no longer instructed to walk thirty metres behind him in public, like he had made Christiaan and me do sometimes when we were little, but I continued to lag. A credulous Gretel trampling the undergrowth. I felt I knew what Paul meant in his poem. The landscape widening within, harriers tracing wind in a bone-marrow sky. The promise of a drought breaking.

Pa came down to the house to listen to the weather report. He put the radio on. "Mooi weer en warm." No rain for us. Some reports of hail in the east. Ma walked in through the happy door and Ouma followed behind with her hair coiffed.

Ma sat down at the breakfast table holding an opened envelope. Ma took her glasses off and buried her face in her hands. Ouma Celia stood in the doorway holding Spokie.

"What's wrong Sandra?" Pa asked.

"Your son has been kicked out of university. He did not write his final exams either."

Pa jumped up. "Let me see the letter."

"You know what this means," Ma said. She pointed to an envelope that lay underneath the letter from the university. It was Paul's call-up papers. He had to report for military duty on the 2nd of January. Ma pulled her pendant from the folds of her blouse and jerked it against its flimsy chain.

Pa ranted up and down the corridor. "What a waste of money! Now he will have to go to the army. That will teach him a lesson. Teach him that actions have consequences!" Pa shouted at all of us. Oupa Bob stood quietly at the sink washing grease off his hands with strong soap. The smell of caramel drifted from the hob. I ran to get the burnt syrup off the stove. Ouma Celia kept stroking Spokie and said, "Ons mooiste en ons slimste. The best one of the lot. I love that child so much. I am bitterly disappointed."

Pa sat down again. "He had better get back here and explain himself. I am not going to be entertaining this indulgence. What he needs is some discipline and routine. Bleddie bederf." Spoilt. We were often described thus. Like fallen fruit below the apricot tree, the flesh too soft and midges swirling.

Ouma Celia adjusted the angle of her jaw in indignant increments. "It's not the Erasmus side of the family that behaves like this," she said. Neither Ouma Celia nor Oupa Bob finished high school.

I slid the bread tins into the oven, closed the door and started walking upstairs.

"Come back here Dominique. Did you know about this?"

"No," I said looking down at the scuffed linoleum tiles of the floor.

"No? No who?" Pa said angrily.

"No, Pa."

"Where's your brother? When last did you speak to him?"

"I haven't spoken to him in a long time. I don't know where he is, Pa."

"A scandal," Ouma Celia said.

"Where's Martha? Where's my tea?"

I put the kettle on and laid a tray. I opened the linen drawer and took out two doilies. One for the sugar bowl and one for the milk jug. They were handmade and hemmed with tiny harp and spindle shells that clinked against the ceramic bowls as I carried the tray into the sitting room. For Pa you had to warm the teapot with hot water and put it on a knitted mat. One bag of English and one bag of Rooibos, the boiling water poured to the brim and a cosy covering it. He liked it just so.

I knew Paul was skipping class and smoking dagga. James had phoned in the middle of the year to speak to Ma but she was not at home. Paul had drifted away from him. James was leaving for England on a scholarship. I had said nothing. Who wants to be an impimpi?

"He must work for me on the farm. That will teach him," Pa said.

I placed the tray in front of him and started walking away. "Aren't you going to pour?" he asked crossly.

Guests unnerved Ma. She fretted in the kitchen and asked me to cut some roses. Ouma Celia told Ma to pull herself together for the sake of the visitors. Auntie Marina and her sisters were coming for afternoon tea to say goodbye before they left for America on holiday. Pa called the Allem sisters "die Roomse Gevaar", and teased them for being observant Catholics. Auntie Marina was Ma's closest friend and lived with her sisters Auntie Dolores and Auntie Juliet in a house as immaculate as the virgin in their rose garden grotto. They ran a shop in town selling silver candlesticks, scent in cut-glass bottles and Madeira linen to farmers' wives. Their farm was called Evening Star. None of them looked their years. Ma took down her Royal Albert from the crockery shelf and said, "The Lebanese understand the value of family. They are better than us."

Ma asked Martha to make scones.

"To think that some people call them sea kaffirs. Not that the National Party is ever shy to ask them for money."

I heard the click-clack down the stone entrance hall of the Aunts in their court shoes. Ma and Pa went to greet them. Conversation swelled in a benign gust of cross-purposes and Pa said, "You lot are like a flock of prattling turkeys, I can't get a word in edgeways." Auntie Marina just laughed at him and commented on the delicious scones. Her perfume was like a velvet rose from Tannie Ester Geldenhuys's famous garden. Auntie Marina asked after Paul. Her nephew was at Princeton.

"That shit is supposedly studying in Cape Town," Pa said. Ma made him promise not to say anything.

"You know Driesie, I do love you, but you must not call your son a shit." Auntie Marina spoke perfect Afrikaans with a St Theresa's Holy Convent of Kroonstad accent. Pa asked Auntie Marina when she was going to make kibbi for him again. Pa loved Levantine food. Auntie Marina would have to debone a leg of lamb, spending hours with a small sharp knife to cut out glands, veins, fat and sinews, then seasoning the chopped meat with crushed wheat, olive oil, mint and spices. "Manna," Pa called it.

"Andries, you're a presumptuous pest to always be asking," Ma said.

Christiaan came into the sitting room with his hand held out. On it lay a large dead cockroach. "Look what I found in the kitchen." Ma went pale with shame.

After the guests left, Pa screamed at Christiaan for embarrassing Ma. She went upstairs and lay on her bed staring at the dam for the rest of the afternoon. Eventually Pa sent me upstairs to go and talk to her.

"Christiaan did that on purpose to shame me in front of the Allems. He learns it from your father."

She got up from her bed.

"I had always hoped your father would treat me with the respect he showed his own mother."

Paul called home from a payphone.

"I'm glad it's you who answered."

"They know what happened at university."

"Shit. I was hoping to get there before the news."

The clatter of coins fed our conversation across distant looping wires. I plaited the twirling cord around my fingers. "Paul, they are really upset and it still has not rained. Pa is furious all the time."

"I am sorry, I should have called."

"Your army papers are here."

Paul kept quiet.

I felt bad about announcing the news triumphantly.

"Mom is trying to get you into Potchefstroom University so you can delay your call-up." I heard Paul strike a match. A statuette from the Free State Farmers' Association sat on the desk next to the telephone. I picked up Pa's trophy. He had designed an implement that made it possible to grow maize in the sandveld. A small plaque on the plinth was inscribed with the words *Andries Botha, Champion of Conservation Tillage – Sand veldt, Northern Free State 1987*. A patent was filed in an office in America, but whether anything would come of it, we had to wait and see. The line crackled. Eventually Paul said, "There's no way I am going to that glorified high school. Forget about it. I'll rather take the army over Christelike Nasionale Onderwys."

"The English professor there said you would be welcome in his department. Pa says you could work weekends on the farm to repay your wasted year at UCT."

"I will repay him. On my terms, but I will do it."

"Where are you now? Are you coming for Christmas? We are going to the sea."

The abrupt drone of a lost connection drowned out his voice.

The Outeniquas were smoky and imposing above a sweep of pencil-blue sea. Tides brought in bluebottles with swept tails, their sting intact. Sometimes the beach was strewn with cabbage-purple seaweed that baked in the sun and stank. Christiaan and I thought that it was an ugly house that Ma and Pa had bought. "Just look at the magnificent setting," Paul used to say. For years the stoep railings rusted through and carpets rotted in the bedrooms because of the damp, and the garden was overgrown with milkwood. Pa was going to fix it all himself when he had the time. Like the road that was washed away at Wolwefontein. Only he could do things properly.

Ma had invited Ishmael Mabitle along for the holidays and Pa flew him down in the Piper Arrow. The friendship tea had led to friendship. He had never seen the sea and could not swim. Ma said not to worry because neither could she. Pa's sister came to the farm to be with Ouma Koeks. She had been in a coma for eight months. Oupa Bob and Ouma Celia were coming down to the sea to look for a retirement home. A replacement for Deur-die-Blare, 6 Boot Street, Pretoria.

Pa was full of enthusiasm for laying the floor in the sitting room. During the year he liked to work and on holiday he liked to work. Or liked to watch others working. Ma had been cross about the cement and the planks lying around. Oupa said, "Andries you must rather build a garage here than fix the floor. You can't insure a car at the coast like one in the interior."

Pa agreed. "It goes without saying. The rust."

Oupa went out to the rocks and fished every day and Christiaan went with him. Black people were not allowed to swim on Central Beach, but Pa said to Ishmael that nobody could accuse him of swimming, the way he just stood with Ma in the shallows. Pa wanted to teach him how to bodysurf. Ishmael laughed at Pa. Ouma never swam, but she sat on the beach in her swimming costume looking far younger than her years. In the early evenings, Ma, Ouma and I prepared Oupa's catch into pickled fish with onions, bay leaves and coriander seeds. Ouma fried the fish fillets in batter before she put them in jars filled with curry sauce.

"I never had anything to do on weekends. If he wasn't fishing, then there was bowls. If not the bowls, then the shooting." Ma looked at me. Ouma always complained about being left alone her whole life for sport. "What your ouma should be doing," Ma said, "is painting." It was not a new counter-suggestion to Ouma's loneliness lament.

I said, "Ma, you can draw just as well. Why don't you do it?"

"I am just a draughtsman, nothing in comparison to your ouma." Ma despaired of Ouma's waste of her talent. Ouma asked for her first glass of sherry. Ma always stiffened as the hour hand slanted upwards.

After a few days there was inevitably a fight and they left for Pretoria before they were meant to. Ouma made Oupa pack their bags and he followed disconsolately in the wake of her assertion, "You won't understand."

Pa said Ouma Celia's mother had been just as bloody miserable as Ouma Celia. "If you think Ouma is bad, you should have known that bitter woman."

Ma said, "You must not forget the tragedy or the shame my mother feels about her parents' divorce."

"In God's name, Sandra are you still a child to believe that rubbish?"

Eunice used to laugh at Ouma. She said we must not judge her: "Old people are like that."

Eunice was very small but she moved around our sofas, cupboards and carpets and swept underneath them every day. She even pushed the piano to and fro. When Pa bought the property, Eunice asked him for a lift and then a job. When Pa left for the Free State, he gave Eunice the keys to the house. She had been with us for more than fifteen years. She left school because of all the toyi-toying in 1976 and because her aunt stole the money her father sent for her schooling to buy beer. She spoke accentless Afrikaans, full of words like *fok, meid* and *moer* when Ma was not around. She wore bracelets of beads and buckskin hidden by her starched uniform.

I went to the yard to hang my underwear on the line. Eunice was sitting on an upended beer crate reading the Bible. She looked at me. "Where's your brother?" I told her that Paul would come some other time. Once Andries calmed down.

Eunice sighed. She said she had a premonition about Paul.

I asked her what she meant by that.

"I dream things."

Portentous things, like her sister's house burning down. She said the dreaming made her sick.

"I went to see a sangoma. He said I would never become better if I didn't become a witchdoctor myself."

She told me she already had people coming to see her. Word of mouth. Mainly coloureds and Xhosas. The coloureds were out on bail and worried about their next hearing in front of the magistrate. She bathed them in warm water in her yard and charged them five rand. They had to tell her everything that they had done. If it was really bad then they were given a special stick to put under their tongues, to help silence the truth in front of the magistrate. That cost more.

"Aren't you scared of those people?"

"Nee wat," she smiled, "I just pray for them and wash them and hear their story. They are happy for that."

I asked her if she prayed for us.

"Never, you don't believe in God." Then she laughed and laughed.

Paul was her favourite.

She said, "I am going to pray for him."

I asked if she would bathe him too.

She said, "That I'll do for free."

The small stone church stood in a copse of flowering gums. Cracked blue shells lay in the conifer spindles. Hymns leaked from the church door, ajar on its wrought-iron brace. Even Ma went with us to the carol service on Christmas Eve, moving along the pew as if bruised. On the way there Ma said the new Dutch Reformed church at the entrance to town was so ugly that God would not deign to live in it. When we got back to the house, Paul stood at the front door. Two nervous faces peered from the seats of an unfamiliar car.

"Aren't your friends getting out?" Pa said. He lived by a sacrosanct edict of hospitality.

"No, they're just dropping me off."

"It would be nice for their families to see them on Christmas." Pa sounded angry.

"They're Jewish. It's immaterial to them."

"In that case," Pa said leaning into the car window, "I insist that you spend the night with us."

"Thanks so much for your offer Mr Botha, but we must press on," one of them said hesitantly.

"Nonsense." Pa opened the car door.

Both had earrings and wore leather jackets. They had the look of the city about them.

"May I present Aaron and Lew," Paul said, returning from the boot with a concrete garden gnome. "I stole this for you from a garden in Port St Johns, Ma. Happy Christmas."

She looked at him with her arms crossed. "Your friends will have to sleep in your room because the spare room floor is still wet with new cement."

Ma and Pa started walking away. Pa turned around and said, "We'll talk in the morning. Go to bed, Dominique."

We went inside and I took out the boiled ham from the fridge and put it on the kitchen table for Paul and his friends. Then I said goodnight and went to bed. I switched on the tattered pagoda-shade lamp I had taken from the sunroom at Wolwefontein.

"So you're the pianist?" Lew asked, walking into the room.

"I play, but I wouldn't describe myself as a pianist," I stammered.

He sat down on the windowsill and patted the pockets of his blue leather jacket for cigarettes.

"Do you mind if I smoke?" he asked, striking a match.

I got out of bed and opened the window to the sound of the counter-marching waves.

"How would you describe yourself, if not as a pianist?" he asked. I could not think of anything to say. My years stacked up like an anaemic résumé of conformity in my mind.

"Probably as Paul's sister, I suppose," I said eventually.

"Fully. Paul Botha is a legend. It's just blowing my mind to be here."

I laughed and smacked a mosquito on my arm.

"Where did you meet?"

"I lived in the Chimney and he was a frequent visitor."

"What's the Chimney?" I asked, getting up to close the window. I pulled my nightie down, it suddenly felt too short.

"Our residence. Known as the Chimney because we were all constantly smoking pot."

"Do you come from Cape Town?" I asked.

"From Johannesburg, but originally from Berlin. The Nazis wiped out my father's family but my grandmother managed to get away. Oaklands is as far as she got." He was thin to the point of skeletal, with pitch-black hair and Prussian blue eyes.

"Ah, man," he said, stretching out his legs and leaning back with his elbows on the piano. "Paul has a real cheek to call us princes from Beverly Hills High. He is, after all, the original barefoot private school boy in chinos. Calling us middle-class …" His voice trailed off as he laughed to himself.

He sat up, struck by a sudden insight. "But that is the amazing thing about him. He has the courage to relinquish the middle-class institutions that no-one else is quite prepared to let go of. To abandon accredited validation, as it were."

"You mean to drop out of university?"

He stood up and cocked his head sideways at my bookshelf.

"Paul epitomises the archetypal beat person. He embodies the nature of the natural outlaw. They are always photogenic. Outlaws always know how to hold a cigarette. He's the guy who does actually get to fuck all the waitresses."

He lit another cigarette, and rested his elbows on the open window as he spoke.

"Paul is obsessed with the material consumptive universe that is currently being refined into common discourse. How corrosive it is to your soul to equate purchasing to personal happiness. Paul wants people to live their subjective truth. He encourages that in everyone he meets. He almost wants to force people to live in a true way."

He pulled out the *Groot Verseboek* from my bookshelf. "At least you Afrikaners have this. The rest of us white South Africans live life like Europe with the sound turned down."

"So what is he going to do now, do you think?" I asked, pulling the sheet across my thighs.

He walked across the room and sat down on my bed. "Continue with what he calls his career as a human being."

Paul walked into the room and looked at Lew. "You can sleep in my room. I'm going to sleep here."

Lew smiled at Paul but did not move.

"Lew has a brain like a television camera. He records and remembers every detail. His acid trip took the whole of the fucking Karoo to relate. Please, no more recollections."

"I don't want you to sleep in my bed. You stink of smoke," I said to Paul.

"What do you mean? Christ! I had a shower." He pulled my head towards his chest. "This is the smell of heaven, darling. And if you don't like the smell of heaven then breathe through your mouth."

"Well, goodnight then, Paul's sister. Cool to have met you." Lew walked out and closed the door.

I lay in the dark, Paul snoring next to me with my pillow over his head. I slowly pulled it back from him. He woke up and said, "I found something I think you will like."

He fumbled for a cassette in his shirt pocket.

"It's this music that's made with rubber bands and telephone dialling tones. Listen."

Paul put it in my cassette player. The volume column rose and fell in little green bars to the strange rhythms and spare melody. I was relieved that I did not have to pretend to like it. I listened to the end of the first track and then turned the volume down.

"What are you going to do without an education?"

"If you are going to be bourgeois, I would rather sleep."

"Paul," I asked as he was drifting back to sleep, "is it normal for people to kiss each other down here?" I pointed to between my legs.

"Are you asking me if it's normal, or if it's normal to like it?"

I blushed in the dark.

"You are almost eighteen years old. Everyone does it."

"Well, how am I supposed to know that?"

Paul sat up.

"Are you sleeping with him, whoever he is?"

"Of course not."

He lit a cigarette.

"For whom did you write that poem in Ouma's recipe book?"

"It doesn't matter."

"Surely you were writing it for someone, whoever she is?"

"Whether it's her or someone else is immaterial. I don't believe in monogamy. In poetry or in life." He put his cigarette butt in my water glass. "So, this boyfriend of yours, does he know what he's doing?"

"What do you mean?"

"Does he know how to undo your bra?"

I laughed.

"As long as it feels good and you like it, then enjoy yourself. Is that not the point of your body?"

I didn't know the answer. It's different for girls. You are not as free.

I woke up to shouting in the dining room. Eunice was in the kitchen, slowly shaking her head. Pa sat at the head of the table waiting for his boiled egg to cool down. "Pa I am really, really sorry." Paul's eyes were red from crying. He pulled out a chair to sit down.

"Your friends have already left," Pa said, pushing the call-up papers over to Paul. Paul just stared at the documents. Christiaan picked up the piece of paper and read out loud.

"Zeerust. Special Services Battalion. Military Intelligence. What a misnomer."

Christiaan put the letter down and picked up another one. "This one is from the Special Battalion Ladies' Association," he said.

Being mothers, we aim to provide support to members of the South African army. We have established a coffee room, which renders the opportunity for open Bible study, spiritual maintenance and well-being. The Army Ladies' Association trusts that you will support your son by looking objectively and positively at army activities. We should always remember that the mother's attitude follows her children to school and therefore to the Army. South Africa desperately needs a positive, hardworking, loyal and persistent youth. Without this, there will be no future in South Africa.

Paul asked if he could smoke at the table.

"Are you ready for this?" Pa barked.

"I don't exactly have a choice, do I? What with the military industrial complex and the Special Battalion Ladies' Association stacked up against me?"

"Don't you have an attitude towards me, sonny boy. You had a choice here. You could still be at university. This is your own fault."

"Did you have compulsory conscription in your day, Pa? Dropping out of Macadamia was my choice. Being forcibly enlisted to murder black people should not be the only counter option. At least spare me the Calvinist hypocrisy of pretending there is some kind of just deserts."

"I suspect your just deserts are on the way. With that kind of attitude you will be finding it a very unpleasant experience."

"I would not have dreamt it differently," Paul said quietly.

We drove home with bottles of seawater, dried apricots from the Little Karoo and three puppies in a box. On the day we left, Eunice arrived at the house with the remnants of her dog's litter. Pa swore and muttered that a hessian sack and some heavy stones would sort out her problem, but Boetie was distraught at the suggestion and Pa yielded.

Paul helped Pa on the farm all week before he left for the army. He spoke little and worked hard. We went across the district to inspect a pile of ruins that Pa had bought. The crumbling stone house on Ruspan lay across the old wagon path from Wolwefontein. Tannie Sarah Geldenhuys sold all the sandstone bricks to Dad on condition that he cleared the site. Tannie Sarah's family had built a new house with aluminium windows on the hill. Pa wanted the bricks to extend the kraal on Wolwefontein. Acacias flowered between the roofless stone walls. An oak tree hinted at a tended garden from long ago. Mud plaster still clung to the walls of dressed stone. Pa was going to mark every brick with a small incision so that he could reassemble them like a puzzle on Wolwefontein.

Pa stood back and knocked his hand against the wooden lintel of the missing front door. "You know my father used to come here as a child on the donkey cart for school. I can't understand why the Geldenhuyse just let this all fall apart."

Paul was peeling away chips of plaster when he shouted, "Come and see this." He had found a glass bottle buried inside a small alcove. Rolled up behind the glass was a yellowed message. Pa helped him to remove the capsule and we took it home with us to Rietpan. We all sat in the sitting room and watched as Pa carefully opened the seal. He fished out the document with tweezers and gently ironed the folios flat with his hands to read.

To whom it may concern,
We, the undersigned, hereby leave a few statements to those surviving ourselves and who in coming generations recover this paper. This document was plastered into its niche in the house of Jan A. Geldenhuys on his farm Rustpan, district Bothaville, on the 8th of April, 1920 in the year of our Lord.

The weather is very promising. In the West a heavy thunderstorm is brewing. The mealies are growing beautifully. The sheep have started lambing. There is a school on the farm.

With kindest wishes to the world at large, we remain your ancestors. The Geldenhuys family and Kleinbaas Preller.

Paul copied the words into his notebook. I could not understand what the fuss was about. Pa said the past matters more to you when you grow old. He put the papers back into the bottle and locked them away in the steel filing cabinet where we kept important documents.

We all went to the train station in Kroonstad to wave Paul goodbye. It was set on a small hill at the edge of the town near the cemetery. The buildings were hand-hewn sandstone like those on Wolwefontein. Pa pointed out the fine workmanship of the stonemasons and said, "Dammit, I never asked my father before he died where they quarried the stone used on Wolwefontein."

The arched entrance led onto a platform where families were standing in small groups under a corrugated iron lean-to. The roof was held up by wrought-iron pillars and sagging balustrades. Segments of broekielace trimming had broken off and chips of flaking enamel paint lay scattered around the ironwork. Slack maintenance irritated Pa. "It's a scandal that this place is being left to ruin," he muttered at the rusting ironwork.

The train arrived with a loud whistling and the sound of metal clanging on worn tracks. It pulled into the station, and Paul looked at us.

"Here goes," he said, quickly disappearing into the throng of uniforms.

CHAPTER 9

Monday 6th
It's raining here. Everybody is in the barracks ... Are you having rain?
What can I say about this place? It exceeds all expectations. We don't start basic training until the 20th but the scrubbing, cleaning, polishing et cetera is going at full steam. Inspection twice a day. Floors must shine. Beds must be square. Dust must dematerialise.
Interesting ride to Joburg station. I shared a compartment with five hardened kaffir-killers to whom pw and Nelson occupy the same niche. From there by cattle truck to a train at some military base. Took another troop train to Zeerust, finally arriving at five in the morning. Spent Saturday klaaring in, getting kit, seeing all the red tape officials could possibly demand, and slept very well that night.

Tuesday 7th
One has very little free time, hence the interruption. We had our medical yesterday. I was classified g1k1 which effectively means fit for everything and gives your corporal licence to do as he wishes, as we found out today. Some people got G5 (exemption) and it's hard to explain the envy with which I watched them, carrying their kit back to the quartermaster's stores, from the queue leading to the barber's chair.
The hills surrounding the security perimeter are beautiful, especially by contrast. Opportunities for transfer present themselves this coming Monday and I am going to be first in line for Anything Else.
How is Dominique?
Must finish off – it's lights out time and this letter must be posted tomorrow.
I love you all and miss you all very much.
Paul

I held Paul's letter to my chest, tapping a scale onto the crinkling pages. Far-off thunder had struck an electrical pole. The fan in the cool room had clanked to a standstill. Crickets were chiselling a precise evensong into the dry night. I lit a citronella candle and looked for a pen. I wondered what to write. Composing a weekly letter had been compulsory at school. This is what happened and then this is what happened next. Ma kept our old letters bound in elastic bands inside a steel filing cabinet in the storeroom. Paul's school letters were full of promises to Pa that he was speaking Afrikaans at his English school.

Liefste Paul, your letter has made me feel sad. You have to believe in vasbyt, min dae.

I scratched out the sentence with the failing ballpoint, its nib blotting and inkless in turn. Ma had the letterhead *Rietpan plaas, Distrik Viljoenskroon* printed onto finely veined and marbled paper. I did not want to throw away her special paper, only for use if circumstance merited it, like the Royal Albert tea set. I turned it over.

Still no rain and Pa is very worried about the crop. The Senekals had an inch last week but here nothing. The Lowveld is having one of the wettest seasons on record, which means our achieved yield will be worth even less. Some good news is that Pa found a spring near the stat on Wolwefontein so now the women won't have to cart water in drums from the river any more. Ma went out to Wolwefontein to bottle figs with Victoria. Swallows have built another nest in the hallway. Ma says she will just let them be. Lang Piet came to the house to send his regards to you especially.

Rietpan's news is that the peahen and peacock finally made a nest after prancing around the garden and showing off for years. Tsietsie found five eggs in it. Can you believe that! The new Labrador puppy came home yesterday with three porcupine quills in his cheek and Dr Kriel had to remove them with pliers. Pa refers to Dr Kriel as that obnoxious pig because, when he went to Wolwefontein to inoculate the Bonsmaras, he removed sugar from the fridge to make way for cattle antibiotics. Pa traced marching ants right up to the fluted lip of the sugar bowl and was furious. Pa said Kriel had no right to do that.

"That" being moving the sugar bowl from inside the fridge to the top of the fridge.

Ma wrote to you about the waenhuis on Wolwefontein burning down. She could have died. Her jersey got caught in the fan belt of the water truck and Christiaan had the foresight to jump on the tractor and push the clutch to stop the jig. Her arm was almost ripped off.

We watched the shed burn and the roof fall. All the old implements and wagons and furniture and beams and that fifty-litre milk churner. All gone.

Pa thinks there was an electrical fault. Christiaan told me that Lang Piet's grandson Shopie had lit a match to see how much petrol was left in the drum in the toolroom because he wanted to steal some. He dropped the match accidently and the drum lit up and blew. Shopie shook so much, Christiaan had to hold him by the shoulders. He told him not to worry about it. Oorlog will never know.

I am feeling much better. Mahudi Tshabalala brought me a Coke bottle filled with brown sludge and bark chips labelled "medsyne vir die kleinmies se gesondhyt". Mahudi and his builders from Witsieshoek are extending the kraal at Wolwefontein with those bricks we got from Ruspan just before you left. They are camping in the abandoned stat and send money home at the end of the month. Ma said there can be no harm in trying his concoction. I swallow a teaspoon a day of the slop that Ma calls Mahudi's good intentions.

It was as disgusting as the remedies from the red-headed homeopath in Vereeniging who undressed me while Ma read a novel in the waiting room full of magazines. I went downstairs to drink the muti in the fridge. Whenever the electricity was cut, the hope was that it would return before the meat in the freezer defrosted and spoilt. Mahudi told me that it was so cold in Witsieshoek that they did not need a fridge. He said, "The Free State winter is nothing." Black people could own land in Witsieshoek because it was a homeland for Sothos with a view of the Amphitheatre from the wrong side. On the other side was the Royal Natal National Park with a whites-only campsite. We went there once hoping to see the famed lammergeyers. Snowmelt drops off the edge of the escarpment and ferns scroll up basalt clefts. Trees surrender and make way for flowering ice plants. On the drive down Pa had told us about climbing through the clouds and seeing the Finger of God. I used to worry that it was blasphemy to talk about God's hands.

I went back to bed to finish the letter.

Paul, don't get into trouble. Ma says it would be best to forfeit your hopes for now, otherwise they will try to crush your spirit. I hope my letter is not too boring for you. I am missing you. A lot.

My body clock had tipped over onto its side. Every night I watched the evening star slowly swindling into the beacon of morning. Paul had told me about Eugène Marais and Hesperian depressions. Baboons got it when the sun went down and leopards prowled in the dark. Paul said that's why humans like Pa drank whiskey at sunset, to assuage a primal anxiety about being eaten. I blew out the candle and lay within the flame's smoky afterthought of struck sulphur and lemon.

I did not tell Paul about John in my letter. When I first heard about him and the other girl, my heart knocked so hard pieces chipped off and fell. Ma said that John was from what English people call "a good family". In Ma's letter to Paul about the failed examinations she called us an honourable family. Elevated adjectives such as *old* and *good* were for Natalians. In Viljoenskroon it was only the town, and then the onderdorp with Jan van der Merwe and his three years in Standard Four. Mr Kruger always used to say that Jan with his hinting moustache and stick-out ears was lucky to live in a time when "the worst white person is better than the best kaffir".

The moon was gliding across the hairline crack of midnight. I laced up a pair of walking boots, climbed out of the window using wisteria branches as footholds and followed the path down to the empty pan. It had not rained for months. I walked along the wenakker seaming the waterside lands. I could chart the boundary lines by heart from the maps in Pa's workshop. All the fields had names. Block A. Block B.

Block C. Vlei Block. Grens Block. Our land was divvied up and parcelled and made manageable. Only watercourses and cattle paths transgressed the parallelograms of planted soil.

I had read Ma and Pa's letter in the joint envelope that was to be posted tomorrow. *My darling son, I am holding thumbs for you and praying and longing to see you. With all my love, Ma.* Pa had written on some threaded printing paper. *We constantly wonder how you are. We are expecting more letters as agreed. Until then, Jou Pa.*

I walked on rolling clover into the cool air that served as tangible memory of the vanished water. Boetebessie had sprung up in the pan's receding wake. Penalty bush. Inspectors used to come round and fine farmers for not destroying the plant. Spreading along watercourses, its tentacle seeds ruined pelts and wool and burrowed to fatally infect the flesh of its host. Pa considered boetebessie the apotheosis of nature's devilry.

I ran the rest of the way to the graveyard on the hill. Cattle huddled silently. Their eyes and breath gave them away. The deranged old man was long gone from the ruins. Grass covered the burial koppie. Smutsvinger. Blou dissel. Olieboom. Kankerroos. Pa loved to stand here when the wind blew and quote the only poem he remembered, "'*Die grassaad aan roere, soos winkende hande.*' Isn't that beautiful? '*Soos winkende hande*'." Grass like beckoning hands in the wind.

I leant back into iron rope swagged above the low cemetery wall. An angel mutely presided over the convocation of jumbled dead. Faded emerald moss flecked her wings. She had lost her haunting reach. The mulberry tree that had fed the silkworms I used to keep as a child still bore fruit in summer. I never tricked them into spinning burgundy threads. The springhares always beat me to the beetroot. Across the empty pan dawn kindled.

Ma banged on the door to wake me up. The teak frames and locks had come from a reclamation yard in Johannesburg years ago and Pa stored the old keys so carefully, he forgot the secret hiding place. I eventually found them in a plastic container marked *Miscellaneous* inside a column of torn tractor tyres. I jumped up and brushed my hair. I never cut it. It grew down to the small of my back and had stayed there, more or less, since I was five. Ouma Celia said I would never find a husband if I did not wear makeup and make more of an effort.

"How are you feeling this morning?" Ma asked as we drove into Rammulotsi. She was taking me to see Ishmael about the township night school. We waited at the four-way stop for Emily Ramile, who was helping with the accounts since Tannie Mariet had moved to Klerksdorp. "Fine," I said, rubbing at the dark rings under my eyes.

People in town had warned Tannie Mariet that the Rietpan Bothas had communist leanings. Paul had a Polaroid picture taken of himself standing at an angle against a wall and wrote *leaning communist* on it. He gave it to Tannie Mariet as a goodbye memento and she cried when she left. Even worse was the alleged presence of a statue of Baal, the false God of the Canaanites, that we worshipped in our entrance hall. Paul laughed so much when Tannie Mariet told him about Baal that he fell on the floor. It made me sad for Pa with his proud suitcase full of family history. To be called a Canaanite idolater.

Emily knocked on the window and I unlocked the passenger door for her. She used to operate the pump at the petrol station in town before Ma employed her. She always dressed beautifully and was fat and sweet and pretty. Even Ouma Celia approved on the proviso that she lost weight. We arrived at the school hall and Ma walked straight to the office. "Bring those forms in the boot of the car," she said, squinting and putting her dark glasses over her prescription lenses. It was too dusty for contacts.

Ma, Ishmael and Father Balink, the Catholic priest, had set up a feeding scheme that was being funded from overseas. Thousands of people queued meekly in long lines on the school grounds three times a week.

"You know, Niekie," Emily puffed as we carried the boxes into the hall, "I can't find a decent man. Black ones always want too many women. White ones only want something sweet on the side."

"What do you mean white ones?" I said, dropping the heavy box on the steel table.

"I mean the legua, Niekie. The white ones. Meidenaaiers." She giggled. "They don't only want to fill the car with petrol. Where do you think the coloured people in the township come from?"

"No way. I don't believe you."

"Stru's bob, Niekie."

I stared at Emily. "Like who, for example?" She leant closer. "Mr Pelser has three children in the township. He loves her and he is kind to them. The children are at a good school in Pretoria."

"I don't believe it. His daughter was in my class."

"Eish Niekie, you will still learn that you can never trust a man."

Ma came walking across the hall with Father Balink and Ishmael. Her Palazzo Pitti heels click-clacked across the cement floor. She bought them once a year in Johannesburg in quiet defiance of her own fears of not having enough money. The food queue was made up of squatters. The town clerk Johan Nel had refused all requests for expansion of the township's boundaries. An illegal land invasion had taken place over night. He woke up to find a new settlement of thousands of people who named their squatter camp Thulanel. It meant Shut up Nel in Sesotho.

I asked Father Balink why the police had not tried to destroy Thulanel. He held his hands together and smiled. "Perhaps they are finally finding their hearts."

Ma said, "Perhaps they are finally losing heart," pushing her glasses closer to her eyes.

"You can neither lose nor find something you never had in the first place," Ishmael said. He believed in education before, during and after liberation. Pa nodded vigorously in agreement whenever he said that. Ishmael's younger brother Abel was in the underground movement and Pa called him Rooi Abel.

Sometimes Rooi Abel knocked on the farmhouse door in the middle of the night and Pa would say, "Hide in the fields. I never saw you tonight. When it's no longer necessary for me to not have seen you, I will send Petrus Maseola on the horse. Away with you." For days Rooi Abel hid in the mielies while Pa gave the police coffee and spoke about fishing in the dam. Emily thought Ishmael was gorgeous but Abel was a rubbish.

Old people and children stood in long lines. Ishmael banished young men queuing because they were too cheeky. Under a shaded lean-to volunteers were ladling out soup and pap from large cast-iron pots. The organisers in Bloemfontein stole two and a half million rand and the European funders wanted to discontinue Operation Hunger. Father Balink and Ma spoke in worried whispers.

Ishmael and I watched an old woman carry her crippled grownup son on her back. Emily gave them a bag of maize and some pilchards in a tin. Ishmael turned to me, "Nel shut off the township's water for a month. That's how he tried to punish the invasion. Ben Zingering opened his garden hose and people with buckets stood in line all the way in to town to get water from his tap. Ben is a good man."

A stone path flanked by succulents led to Ishmael's office door. He offered tea in transparent cups and saucers made by Oranje Potteries next to the silos on the outskirts of town. They were in danger of being shut down by union demands.

When Pa heard that he was outraged. "Can you bloody well believe it? Rather nobody must have a job than somebody operate a sustainable business." I poured milk to the brim and one sugar. Maths papers were piled up on Ishmael's desk.

"So," he said, leaning back in his chair, "do you think you can teach adults English?" Emily was right about Ishmael being good looking. "I am not really qualified. I've just matriculated."

He smacked his desk with both hands, "That qualifies you. These adults cannot even read or write, but they have a wish to better themselves."

"When do I start?"

He smiled. "Tonight if possible. Classes begin at six and end at eight." He filled my name into the empty slots in his teaching schedule.

I looked out the window at the patrolling police vehicles. There were more than usual. Unrest. Stones had been thrown at the municipal offices. A child had been shot. Self-defence was the state's case. The lawyer for human rights who came down from Johannesburg scratched his head, while Pa made Goldberg throw bricks at a distant meerkat from behind a line in the sand. To demonstrate the impossibility of lobbing a missile that distance. Pa had not forgotten the statutes in his textbooks.

"How is Paul doing in Satan's army?" Ishmael asked. He stood up to open the door for me, the completed schedule in hand.

"We haven't heard much from him. Satan seems to be a hard taskmaster."

"We'll vanquish him yet," he said, and hugged me goodbye.

It took much cajoling before Pa allowed me to drive from Rietpan to the township by myself at night. I liked teaching. The township grew more beautiful in the dark. Murmuring voices of people walking home. A fruit tree in every yard. Moonlight softening the corrugated constructions. My pupils were older than Ma and Pa. I asked for histories of their lives. To see where to pitch the lessons in literacy. I sat at my desk with a view across the dry pan, reading their work. A flock of kwikstertjies flew past the window. One woman had been tea lady for the cabinetmaker in town. She was asked to take a cheque to the bank and then changed it into her name in the broom cupboard with a red pen. Three years in Kroonstad prison. She wrote that she would never do that again.

Pa said all the birds massing like this at sunset could mean that rain was on the way. I was alone in the house. Pa was up at the workshop and Christiaan was at Wolwefontein digging up the French drain under Cardow's supervision. He had been expelled from Hilton for a nihilistic attitude. He had bunked out to visit a sick friend in hospital. The headmaster said there seemed to be something wrong with all the Botha children. Apparently Pa stood up and said, "Thank you very much, that is an insult beyond the pale."

The French drains bled away past the water tank towards a copse of pepper trees. They remain verdant all year.

I took my diary from underneath my mattress.

We live at the heart of a great and fatal sin. A shattered command-
ment. A delusional morality is siphoned from neat rows of well-kept
fields and skirts hemmed below the knee and an unquestioned belief in
an absurdly partisan God. Full stop. Juffrou Cora is a stupid bitch.
Full stop.

Juffrou Cora had cornered me in the supermarket with her arms around my waist and said, "I hear you teach kaffirs how to read at night. The men in my family would never tolerate such a thing." She squeezed me even harder and whispered, "I don't know how you can stand the smell." Behind her a carcass of beef was being stripped of its marbled fat. Her perfume gave over-generously of itself.

"Despite the lack of running water and dust, the shacks are as clean as Juffrou's own house that is scrubbed daily by the same dirty, stinking kaffirs." She gave a hard smile and let me go. I stumbled down the aisle. Juffrou Cora shouted after me, "Those English schools. Mark my words, nothing good will come of it!"

Ma always used to speak out when she could just have walked away. She always bought from the black side of the shop and told the Indians across the Vaal that they must not call their help "stupid kaffertjies" in order to impress her. It was always very embarrassing when Ma made a fuss. She once told me that was one of the things she first liked about Pa. That he was not a racist. "He used to be a very good-looking man, your father. He still is." I often wondered what they had in common other than an interest in universal franchise.

People muttered that we Bothas thought we were too good for Salomon Senekal. I sometimes stayed with Ouma Koeks in town. Juffrou Cora's laatlammetjie brother Gys would sneak out of the hostel and knock on my window. We climbed up the seringa tree on the pavement outside Ouma's house and watched police vans drive by in the dark. I swung my legs and Gys smoked cigarettes and he always said, "Hoog in die takke is 'n lekker plek om te wees." He was brave to smoke. Mr Kruger used to cane the matric boys into the doctor's rooms for a minor infraction of hair over their ears. Sometimes Gys left hibiscus flowers on Ouma's doorstep that he stole from Auntie

Pauline's garden. That was the most beautiful garden in town by far. Herbaceous borders spilling onto mown grass, alyssum and roses and clematis and camellias. The bride of the garden was a magnolia with blossoms like teacups on saucers. Gys never used the K word, not once, or at any rate never in front of me.

I wondered where Gys was now. I put my pen down. Pa's footsteps in the hall meant the end of the farm's working day. I put my diary under my mattress and went downstairs. Pa sat back in a steel garden chair on the stoep, stretching his legs and pointing at the vlei. "I can think of no better place in the world to be." He always drank one whiskey at sunset. Selina used to lay out the tray every evening with the ice bucket and a small bowl of cut biltong. Now Martha did.

I sat next to him in the darkening afternoon. Cloudbanks pulled open a slit onto the dying day. The vlei rang with birdsong. Pa put a doily over his glass to keep moths from drowning in his whiskey.

Ma came back from a cattle auction in Bothaville and stood behind Pa's chair with a cup of tea in her hand, stooping in the way of a woman who wants to shrink. Ma grew up in a time when it was unfashionable for women to be tall. Ma said, "Boetie wants to go with Firi on the Waaisand school tour." It was to be the first ever tour for our farm school. Pupils had been raising funds for over a year to rent a bus for three days to go to the Northern Transvaal. I bought stale popcorn from them in Checkers packets.

Pa sighed. "Let him go. It will spare me further irritation. It might even be good for the little shit."

In the morning Pa had instructed Boetie to go with Christiaan to Wolwefontein, and Boetie hid under the bed until they gave up looking and left without him. If Pa asked Boetie to look for his glasses, Firi found them. If Ma told Boetie to clean his room then Firi did it. Firi called them Mamma and Pappa in the Sotho manner of Ntate and Mme. Firi said the other workers tried to toor Cardow out of jealousy but his blood was too strong. Later Firi and Boetie asked for pocket money for the tour and Pa made them pull out opslagmielies for spare change. Boetie lay under the red wagon in the shade reading comics while Firi and the older labourers filled hessian sacks with weeds and

Nadia went round and round the horse circle Pa made for her near the ambulance carcass overgrown in prickly pear. All our wagons were painted the colour of stoepverf.

The new school principal Mr Patsa said Ma must not worry about Boetie going along, but, because of the State of Emergency, she did. Boetie also still wet his bed sometimes and could not tie his shoelaces.

There was a loud knock on the door. "Who the hell would that be now?" Pa muttered as he walked across the stone floor of the entrance hall. Labourers only ever came to the back kitchen door. Male voices echoed in the hall. I saw blue uniforms in the doorway. "Thank you, commander. I will make enquiries. Hopefully we can even leave tonight."

"Who was that at the door, Andries?" Ma asked.

"Pieter van Vuuren."

The chief of police.

"Paul's gone AWOL. Pieter says the military police are looking for him."

Pa sat down. "Dammit," he said, putting his hands in his hair.

It was still but for fluting plovers below the willows. "What's going to happen to Paul?" I asked.

"Pieter says if he goes back voluntarily it would be much better than if the military police locate him. He offered to help me find him before the MPs do. Van Vuuren is a decent man."

"If you take him back, what happens then?" Ma asked, composure draining from her voice.

"They will put him in military prison. It's supposed to be worse than civilian jail. But at least the punishment will be less severe if he returns voluntarily with me."

Pa looked up. "Now we have to find him. Do you have any idea where he might be?"

I looked at Pa. "If I find out, can I come with to fetch him?"

"Definitely not."

I found Lew's number scrawled in the margins of my notebook and called him in Johannesburg. Paul had been in Hillbrow with someone called Jonathan. "That guy Jonathan is off the fucking rails man.

They've gone to Pietermaritzburg to stay with Rick Schultz. Just don't tell anybody I told you."

I told Pa that Rick was the one whose parents met as outpatients at Valkenberg. Pa said, "Ag, Here." The police chief came back to the farm later that night in his wife's car. She dropped him off and gave them a flask of coffee and some sandwiches. After Pa left and Ma went to bed, I dialled Rick's number again and this time the call was answered.

"Hello, this is Dominique. Paul's sister."

"Paul, you have been apprehended by the matronly police."

Paul took the receiver, "Hello my sweet sister. It's good to hear your sweet voice."

"Are you drunk?"

He laughed, "Drunk is such a vulgar word. I love you. Come and join us."

"Pa is on his way to fetch you." I was whispering so that Ma would not hear. The wooden staircase snapped and groaned in the entrance hall.

"I am going to a party later tonight, so I can't go back with Pa. Sorry. I also promised Rick I'd mow the lawn tomorrow."

"Paul, are you insane? The military police are looking for you."

"Let them find me. They must do their work. They are wasting taxpayer's money if they don't." He laughed.

"Please just come. It's better this way, I promise," I pleaded. "They are going to put you in something that is worse than civilian jail. Please just come home with Pa."

Ma fell over the Labrador puppy with the tea tray. She wept about the accident as if there had been news of a death. We all stood around embarrassed. Paul started picking up the broken china, but Pa said, "Sit down. I've not finished talking." Pa told Ma to pull herself together. "It's only a thing, we have other teapots."

She cried and shouted at him, "It is our wedding gift that I treasured most, Andries. It's more than a replaceable thing." Then she ran outside.

We sat in a row on the sofa in the sitting room not looking at each other. Christiaan, Paul and I. Pa was calmer after Ma broke her tea-pot. I had thought he was going to hit Paul when they came back from Natal that morning. He finished every sentence with the question, "You hear me?" Eventually he stopped ranting and took the china pieces up to the workshop.

Paul waited in the courtyard for Pa to take him back to Zeerust.

Yellowing arteries of glue crisscrossed bouquets of burgundy roses on the mended teacups, drying on the windowsill.

CHAPTER 10

The day after Paul slit his wrists, the drought broke. Rain came as if seeking absolution. Lightning struck at the foundations of the house. Wind tore roofing off the shed. Felled cattle and blue gums lay in its wake. At first hardened earth resists the hammering rain but the bare veld is defenceless and starts bleeding between remaining clumps of rooigras. Slow streams grow into torrents that swallow roads, fords and livestock. The False River lived up to its name and broke its banks. Wolwefontein was mired. Inaccessible.

Pa said when the Gods seek to punish you, they answer your prayers. It can rain for days. Martha took down rows of polished brass candlesticks from the pantry shelf. The generator was fired up in the workshop to power the welding machine and fuel pump. Moss crept into flagstone grouting. Trees gave thanks. That was how I imagined Europe. Wet and cold with cypress spires, tapering to smudged ink.

Christiaan, Ma and I sat around the kitchen table. We waited for the sound of the returning bakkie down the driveway. Pa was notified to collect Paul from the railway station in Kroonstad. He was granted three days' leave of absence before reporting to the army hospital in Pretoria. His behaviour warranted psychiatric evaluation. "A serious suicide attempt is where veins are slit longitudinally deep into the groove that runs towards the joint," Ma said, holding her arm up to the candle. "A slash across the wrist is more attention-seeking than anything else." I looked at Christiaan and he looked away. "After everything we have been through with the AWOL. Your father having to search for him like a fugitive at the height of the planting season. I don't understand it." Ma got up and put a pot of water on the paraffin stove to boil for tea. Washed wind seeped in below the door. I shivered and Ma told me to fetch a jersey.

Tannie Rina at the post office said a soldier's body was the property of the state. She knew of someone who was tried for vandalism after shooting himself in the leg on purpose. Pa had sent me to fetch the post while he went to the co-op to buy poison to lace stagnant pools around the house full of breeding mosquitos. I asked Pa about the wilful damage to state property. He said, "Pay no attention to that odious birdbrain Rina." He wound up the window and drove off to Kroonstad.

Ma poured us a cup of tea. I fetched a pullover from the laundry and brought the kittens through to the kitchen. I kept them in a basket next to the asbestos heater in the laundry. I poured milk into a cracked saucer. The kittens stepped in and out of the milk, shaking wet paws on the tablecloth. "Pa won't like this," Christiaan said. Pa hated cats and fixated on cracks in porcelain that might harbour meningitis. Ma sighed. We cleaned their infected eyes with cotton wool and hot water and then Ma took the three mewling kittens back to the laundry and shut the door.

Paul had flayed his veins up to the elbow joint with a discarded razor he found in the detention barracks shower. The guard noticed the water running red into the communal sluice. The army doctor sewed him up and sent him back to DB. That's what Pa told us.

Pinky, Ouma Koeks's arthritic Labrador, lay under the kitchen table with special dispensation at night. During the day she barked at the wind from the back of Pa's bakkie. Pa relented to the dog's ardent affection and called her "my honne". I pulled the curtain back and saw the moon. The rain had let up. Once the clouds pull clear of the stars, a mating dirge of lily frogs and platannas meld into an incessant percussive din. Pinky stood up. Pa started shouting instructions from outside.

"Christiaan, get your brother's suitcase from the bakkie then go and lock up the workshop. Sandra make some tea. Beyond Aandson the floodgates have opened. That rain is on its way here."

Pa came hurrying in holding the door open. Paul walked in slowly. He wore browns and boots without laces. His arms were heavily bandaged beyond the elbows. I lay my head between his shoulder blades in greeting, away from his shredded arms. Pinky muzzled Pa's leg. Pa said, "Wait now, my honne, wait now." Ma put her hand up to Paul's face. She shook her head and walked away to the scullery.

"Dominique, take your brother's bag upstairs," Pa said. Ma turned around. "That's a man's job." Pa looked at her in wearied irritation, "For God's sake Sandra." He took the bag from me.

Paul sat down at the foot of the staircase. "We saw jackals," he said, "when we drove onto the farm there was a family of five black-backed jackals on the road. They just stood there. I have never seen them so unafraid. Then there was a clap of thunder and they were gone. Instantly."

"Yes, it's true, you know, Sandra," Pa said, his irritation dissipating, "and tell your mom we also saw kudu next to the pan. Since that Van der Spuy bastard started shooting, they have become so wary."

Paul smiled, "There was a huge bull with beautiful horns."

"That's lucky," Ma said. She pulled at the pendant hanging round her neck. She looked down at her hands and said, "Would you like some dinner?"

"No thank you, Ma. I just want to go and lie down."

"Listen son," Pa said, "you must get cleaned up first. Dominique, go and run our bath."

Paul slowly followed Pa down the passage. I walked ahead cupping a flickering candle, illuminating hallway ancestors. They no longer climbed out of their frames at night but disapproval still leaked from their fading profiles. Men in black suits with pinned carnations. Stout women with straining corsets. Babies like pastel dolls on wicker chairs in studios full of palm fronds.

I placed the candle in front of the bathroom mirror and turned open the taps. It set off a volley of clacking shots that scattered pigeons from the roof. The sound transfigured into a looping song of whistles and sighs. Pa said it was the excessive pressure setting. Or maybe the washers were worn through. As the copper warmed, the voices in the pipes trailed to a whisper.

"I remember the singing pipes. I haven't bathed here for years," Paul said.

I watched as Pa undressed Paul.

"I am still going to fix that bloody noise," Pa said. "That idiot from Klerksdorp who installed the geysers was a charlatan."

"Don't fix it. I like it Pa. The house has its own voice," I said, looking up at him.

He sighed. "Women can talk a lot of nonsense."

Paul laughed. He was much taller than Pa. He had inherited Ma's height. Before Pa left for Kroonstad, he said, "Sandra, you must help me here. I fear Paul's nature knows no boundaries." Ma said she really did not know what to say.

Pa methodically removed Paul's shirt not to aggravate the dressing. "Fixing the pipes should not be a priority, Andries," Ma said, holding Oupa's flannel pajamas and a jug of boiled water to add to the bath.

"Fetch some fresh soap," Pa told me and chucked the sliver of Pears into the dustbin. Paul sat on the edge of the bath and Pa pulled thick-soled boots off his feet. Pa complained that his socks stank.

Paul laughed, "I wasn't at finishing school. I'll just get into the water like this." He got up and stood barefoot next to the bath, wearing only army pants.

"Don't be bloody ridiculous, son. Let's do this properly." Pa loosened the buckle of Paul's belt and pulled his trousers down below his knees. Paul stepped out his browns and stood naked next to the bath. His chest was pale and smooth like a child's, but the outline of his body was that of a man. His feet were long and narrow with a high instep. Ma said that is the first thing she noticed in other people, and the first thing she noticed in Paul when he was born, his beautiful little hands and feet.

He climbed into the water with his arms above his head. I held his hands to lessen the strain while Pa scrubbed his back. The doctor said not to get the dressings wet. Pa washed Paul's underarms and he pulled away laughing. "Don't move, dammit," Pa said.

"Then don't tickle me," Paul laughed, but there were tears on his cheeks.

Pa said, "Get out now." Pa dried him and helped him into Oupa's pajamas.

Ma picked up the candle. "I put some tea next to your bed." They walked with Paul past the rooms where Nadia and Boetie were fast asleep. Christiaan and I stood in the doorway watching as Pa helped him lie down.

Pa put an extra blanket on the bed, switched off the lights and ushered us into the passage. "Night, son," he said to Paul as he pulled the door closed. "You two as well. Go to bed. It's late."

The rain had returned with less urgency. It was the rain we needed. Soft and penetrating, not the angry flood from before. Sleeping country lit for miles around by lightning. A soft-throated incantation of leaking gutters. Christiaan and I waited until Ma and Pa went to sleep. We went into the room and tiptoed to the bed.

"Paul, are you awake?" I whispered.

His eyes were wide open. "Christiaan please open my window," he said. The fresh incense of broken drought drifted into the room. I sat on the end of Paul's bed, careful not to shift the mattress. The eiderdown that Johnny and Kobus had burnt cigarette holes through was patched with white cotton and rolled up at the foot of the bed. Those little white spots always made me think of Kobus and what might have happened. Christiaan took a box of cigarettes out of Paul's tog bag.

"Can I light one for you?" he asked.

Paul edged up against the headboard. "Please." Christiaan lit a cigarette and held it to Paul's mouth. He took a deep puff. Christiaan took the cigarette from Paul's lips and put it in the ashtray next to the bed. We sat quietly as Christiaan kept bringing the cigarette to Paul's lips. He smoked while we waited in the dark for him to finish.

"Does it hurt a lot?" I asked.

Paul blew a smoke ring. "It hurts more now than when I did it." He winced as he adjusted his posture in the bed.

"Was it that terrible to be in DB?" Christiaan asked hesitantly.

Paul laughed softly. "Not really any worse than being in the army proper, just a variation on an already grim tune."

Paul finished the cigarette and Christiaan stubbed it in the ashtray. Occasional shafts of pallid light lit the dark room.

"They sent a dominee to come and see me before I got put on the train. The dominee called me 'son', but I don't think he was over thirty.

He had worked in the platteland for ten years from the time he was ordained in the Western Transvaal. He went on huisbesoek to outlying farms at night and always stopped at the four-way crossings and counted to ten. Please light me another one."

He took the cigarette with his shaking arm and lay down holding it to his chest.

"This dominee explained to me that, although the roads are always deserted at night, and the landscape is so flat one could see for miles, he always stopped and counted to ten." Paul blew a smoke ring and paused.

"If he had read my file, the fucking zealot would have seen that I was from the Northern Free State. I know the damn landscape better than him. But listen to this: he knew that although no-one else would see him cross without stopping, God could see him. That was his allegory for me in my so-called hour of need. Jesus Christ, I need a drink just thinking about it."

"You could have died," Christiaan said.

"Or worse. They gave me a pencil and paper to write my own defence for the trial. I thought long and hard about poking my eyes out. I worried that the pencil might miss my brain and I would survive blinded. Then they would make me tune pianos for seven years as an unconscientious objector."

Paul laughed. "Now I am going to be taken in front of a psychiatric tribunal instead of a military one."

"Which is worse?" I asked.

"The one with the most experts. The professorial avatars of Christian Nationalism, so to speak. Covered to the eyeballs in their own hubris."

"Are you scared?" Christiaan asked.

"Are you joking? Fuck them. I feel nothing." He sounded tired.

"At least we will be allowed to visit you in the military hospital," I said.

"I will be there under observation. So come and observe."

"I think we should leave now," I said, getting up. "Do you want me to close the window?"

"Please don't. I like the sound of the rain."

Christiaan looked at me. "I'm staying."

Paul groaned softly as he huddled under the blanket and turned to face the wall.

Paul was in Pretoria for a fortnight before Ma and I went up to see him. We never went there any more since Oupa Bob and Ouma Celia had moved to Knysna and named their new house Nog-meer-deur-die-Blare, after the old one. I remembered the lattice of flowering avenues and flamboyant birds. Oupa and Ouma bought their first house in Waterkloof when Ma turned eighteen. Ma said Ouma worked her way up from nothing so that they could live with some decency.

We signed in at the hospital entrance and were directed to Paul's ward. An old woman with her knees padded in rags was scrubbing linoleum tiles in the corridor with Cobra wax. Ma greeted her in Sesotho but she kept her head down and kept polishing. The ward sister took me to Paul. Ma was late for her meeting with the psychiatrist, so I went alone. Paul's ward was off to the left with a bank of small windows set just below the high ceiling. He lay in a narrow bed alongside nineteen other men in pyjamas and nightgowns. They were not allowed to change into day clothes.

I lifted a white paper box from the basket I had placed under his bed. "I made you a chocolate cake." Paul had a sweet tooth. "I have a supply of boxes now because I am baking for the tuisnywerheid again." I held the cake up for him. I felt the eyes of the ward boring right through my sleeveless dress. "I buy supplies wholesale in Klerksdorp from an Indian trader. Tannie Ronnie gave me his details. He has a tiny shop but it's piled high with coconut, maraschino cherries, castor sugar, everything you could possibly need."

Paul smiled.

"I made these myself," I said, blushing and pointing to the chocolate leaves on the cake. "I pick ivy leaves off the outside wall of the kitchen, wash them and then coat them with melted chocolate." I sat down on the visitor's stool next to his bed.

Paul picked a leaf off the cake and put it into his mouth. "Go on," he said.

I shifted around on the uncomfortable chair. "I put the coated leaves in the cool room to harden. Not too long, otherwise the chocolate discolours. Then you peel back the leaf and the shape remains imprinted. Can you see?" I held the cake closer.

"Fuck me, I would love a piece of your cake," one of the men shouted from across the ward.

Paul laughed, "Fuck off. She's my sister, you demented pervert."

He leant towards me. "That poor motherfucker went bossies. They will just pump him full of drugs and send him back to the border. He probably hasn't seen a fuckable woman in months."

He leant closer and whispered into my ear. "Everyone here is drugged. Sleeping pills, anti-anxiety pills, copper sulphate, lithium, the works. I put their cocktail under my tongue and pretend to swallow. It's the first time in my life I have actually avoided taking drugs."

He lay back and laughed.

"Aren't the types of drugs they give you here supposed to help?"

"Don't be bloody stupid. They don't give a fuck about rehabilitation. They just want everybody bloodthirsty enough to kill. Anyone who doesn't comply is considered mad. They treat us with veterinary drugs and art therapy. Jesus, you should see the poppie teaching us pottery. Everyone is so jags we just want to gang rape that little missionary."

"How did the tribunal go?" I asked. "Are they going to send you back to military jail?"

"Dunno, we'll find out tomorrow." He suddenly seemed tired.

"What did those men on the tribunal ask you?"

"Well," he said, "I sat in front of a panel of white men in white coats. Probably macademics from the univershitty over there." He pointed to where a vast monolith of distance learning stood on a hill behind the ward's grey walls.

"They asked me if I ever harboured sexual thoughts towards other men. I said certainly not towards any of them. I said I pretty much wanted to fuck everybody else. Especially their wives, their daughters and their other domestic servants."

He sat up again.

"I also told them that if their university learning had taught them anything, it surely would have been the value of self-reflection. Could they reasonably ask me if I was mad? Did it not perhaps occur to them that they were mad? Supporting and upholding as they do, the madness of our times?"

He shouted, "To be told I have damaged military property, my own body! Can you fucking believe that?"

The nurses were staring at us from their cubicle.

"I told them, 'You people are in no motherfucking position to judge my sanity. You are fucking mad. You guys. Not me.'"

"Calm down, Paulie, don't speak so loudly." I put my hand on his shoulder. He pushed it away.

"Is it not self-evident who should be the ones being brought in front of a panel? When their God they are so breathlessly kowtowing to finally wakes up to the misdemeanours of His second chosen race. Hopefully to take them out for the good whipping they deserve." He lay back.

"Have you finished shouting?" I asked.

"I have finished," he said.

"I brought you some cigarettes and money from Christiaan. He's gone back to school. Also some books."

"Thank God." He grabbed the novels. "All they give you here to read is the Bible. I found a King James version in the so-called library. There is some hair-raising stuff in there man. I've kept the bits I like the most."

He pulled out sheaves of folded gilt-edged paper from his pocket. The kind that crinkles when you turn the pages. Ma used to get furious if we so much as bent a triangle to mark a page.

"I can't believe you did that, Paul. That's vandalism."

"Rubbish man, to tear pages out of a novel is inconsiderate, I agree. But no-one reads the Bible chronologically. I can assure you it's heresy that will go unnoticed."

A bell rang. It was the end of visiting hours.

"Please tell Christiaan I say thanks. I pity the poor bastard having to go back to school. Funny how restrained he is. Saving pocket money, even bloody Easter eggs. Must be a weird but useful quality to have."

His arms were still bandaged. They had cleaned the wounds and replaced the dressings.

Ma came into the ward. "We will hear tomorrow," she said to Paul. "The psychiatrist said you were not very co-operative. He mentioned things like an attitude problem. Issues with authority. These are not unfamiliar accusations, Paul. Perhaps it's time that you see your perspective is that of the minority."

"Well, is it not the minority perspective that counts round here, Ma?"

Ma folded her arms across her chest. "Sies Paul, look how dirty your fingernails are."

A nurse came to call us away.

Ma drove fast. The sky darkened into another oncoming storm. The hoped-for rain was turning into a curse. Farming is always either feast or famine. There was no chance of getting the tractors into the lands. "Maybe your father will plant some wheat this winter." Pa sometimes risked growing a winter crop after very wet summers on the fields slanting down to the pan. When we turned onto the farm road, Ma stopped the car. "I can't see anything. My glasses are misting up."

I opened the door into the downpour, ran around the front and took over the driving. Ma pleaded for me to be careful, the wheels churning through a deepening onslaught of mud and darkness. Pa was waiting for us in the driveway. "I told you to leave Pretoria earlier. I was so concerned. Why is the child driving? Jesus Sandra, you can be so irresponsible." I left them to the sparring they had substituted for love.

I walked upstairs to the bathroom and locked the door. I stood in front of the mirror. I had made my dress from a bolt of floral cotton that had been in Ma's storeroom for years. I pulled off the wet cloth moulded over my shoulders. I lit a candle, turned on the taps and sat on the edge of the bath, letting the water run through my fingers. I did not think that attempting suicide was cowardly. I thought Paul was brave. I scooped a drowning spider out of the bath.

The hospital ward made me think about John. All those men. Prowling. I was ashamed about mourning his indifference so keenly. In truth we had so little to say to each other. I wanted to kiss him. To feel his weight on me, his hands in the small of my back, lifting me towards him. I climbed into the bath and slowly swayed my legs, the water curling through my thighs where they folded into conclusion. I put my hand between my legs where John used to kiss me. On my sweet, wet cunt, as he used to say, until the dense pleasure broke and pulsed away. I laughed at myself. I never knew that lust could be its own handmaiden. Coming. Too prosaic a word for that point of arrival that in men was an accessory to the creation of new life. John and I only did it once. My bloodied sheet anonymous in the drying yard of secrets.

It had triggered the loss of him. My sweet cunt of a first boyfriend. His infidelity suddenly there again like a glass shard in my chest. I lay there listening to the sky opening her sluices. The tin roof a cymbal and water felted mallets. I retraced his last journey in my mind and in my diary. How he had hitchhiked from university to plead for forgiveness. How we lay together in the dark house while Ma and Pa slept. An impaled snowbird and a flute player with cloven feet. I wished him ill. I wished him within me still.

Ma and Pa came into my bedroom the next morning. I had overslept. Ma opened the curtains and I pulled the sheet over my nakedness. Her eyes were red and Pa looked haggard.

"What's wrong?"

"There has been a terrible accident."

"Where's Paul?"

"That's another story."

Pa stood at the window. "Dominique, Ishmael died last night. His car overturned on the road to Orkney into a ditch. He drowned. Trapped."

"These are terrible times," Ma cried softly. She held her hands up despairingly. "People live here facing into the wind."

Pa walked to the door, "He was one of the finest people I ever knew. I am going to fetch Paul."

I sat up. "Has Paul been given permission to come to the funeral?"

"He's been given permanent permission to leave the army. He's been dishonourably discharged. Physically and mentally unfit to be a member of the armed forces. They call it a G5K5."

"That's good news. It means he won't go to jail? It mean's he is free?"

"What it means, Dominique," Pa said wearily, "is that he will never be able to find a job with that mark against his record. It will be an indelible stain."

I sat by the window looking out across the pan. April clouds pressed in ash. The funeral was the biggest in township memory. Pa had not wanted to go to the house afterwards. To be treated like royalty for no good reason but that we were white and we were there. But we went. Plates of marog and stew in a striped tent in Ishmael's yard and his coffin under a heap of clods in the cemetery. The school was closed until further notice. Ishmael's office door bolted and the curtains drawn. No more night school. To Ma, Ishmael had led an exemplary life. A life she wanted her children to emulate.

I got up and walked to Paul's room. He was sitting in the corner reading, his packing abandoned. The evidence of his initial effort lay on his bed. Some of Oupa Boetie's safari suits neatly folded, a carton of cigarettes, notebooks and photographs filched from the family albums. Ma wearing a swimming costume in front of the old house at Klein Rietpan, very pregnant with Paul. A leather suitcase leant against the bed with tan straps and a name embossed in raised leather. *Paul Michiel Botha, Wolwefontein Plaas, Republiek van die Oranje-Vrijstaat.* "Does Pa know you are taking Oupa's stuff?" I asked, sitting down on his bed. Paul took a ballpoint pen and drew the Roman numeral for six next to the pressed name. He enclosed the numeral in brackets.

"You can't just do that. Pa's going to be furious."

"What's he going to do? Gate me?"

Ma and Pa disapproved of Paul's plans. Or rather the lack thereof. Paul was not getting another cent from Pa.

"Where are you going to go?"

"I know some people in Johannesburg. I am hitching tomorrow morning."

Paul snapped the old silver buckles shut.

"Let's go to Wolwefontein. The river is in flood."

"We must ask Pa if we can take the truck. They are sleeping."

Paul just laughed. I reluctantly followed him down the hallway. He took the International truck key from the rack. Oupa Bob had wrought the hooks into a small piece of yellowwood and given it to Ma as a Christmas gift. Our house was full of his weekend handiwork. Furniture, slingshots for Christiaan and a model soccer team welded from lead for Paul. A true artist, Pa called him.

Paul pushed the shed door open. Oupa Boetie had imported the International truck from America after the Second World War. It was no longer possible to buy parts because of sanctions and it had to be looked after very carefully. According to Pa all American cars were big. The grumbling engine loosened dust and stones from the chassis. We drove on gliding suspension straight into the late afternoon sun.

At the turn-off to Wolwefontein, the cropped plain folded away to thorn veld. Along verges khakibos turned spiky below shimmering poplars, and cosmos peeped white and pink through blonde grass on tender stems flecked with butterflies. Clouds formed a watercolour in the distance. A korhaan flew up and made its kê-kê-kê alarm call.

I turned the radio on. Klassieke Keur on Radio Oranje.

Paul turned the volume up. "Whatever this is, it rocks," he said.

I looked at him and smiled.

Heavy tractor wheels had churned the farm road into a morass of black pot clay. Paul guessed at the hard verge leaving behind a swerving track through the mud. Pa was going to rebuild the road. With a perfect camber. Like the Romans built roads.

Every time we stopped at a gate, I got out and pushed it clear so Paul could drive through. The easy ones were the heavy, cantilevered types that swung on creaking hinges. The bekslaners between cattle paddocks were trickier. The lock was a wooden plank looped taut around a post and fixed with a snag to brace the sagging wire. We called them oppas gates because Pa used to shout "oppas" from the driver's seat when we fiddled too long in opening.

Paul drove the truck onto a spit of land above the bend in the river.

"Where's the road gone?" I asked, looking around.

"It's below there," Paul said, gesturing towards the swollen water. The road lay buried beneath the deluge. He plucked a long stem of weeping grass and chewed the soft ends of the shoot.

"Last July I quarried sand for Pa. Up and down, up and down the riverbed. The road is practically grooved in my brain." In winter it was a river in memory only. The watercourse is plastered in a skin of wrinkled mud. Tractors could get right down to the riverbed. Pa sold the sand to the Roads Department. According to Pa ours was excellent sand and we deserved the premium paid for it. I sat down on a rusting scrap ripper.

Flooding left a shallow lake with a marooned acacia copse covered in egrets on the plain below the opstal. A fat Bonsmara bull lazily flicked his tail at some starlings. Intermittent thunder rumbled in solitary clouds. I watched dragonflies chase mosquitos in a grass-choked eddy. Pond Damsels, Dancing Jewels, Vagrant Emperors. Paul lay down with his head on the caving rim of a sandstone saltlick. Butterflies massed on the renosterbos weed nearby.

Paul stretched out his arms and yawned, "Fuck all happens here except the slow ticking of a natural clock."

A sacred ibis flock lowered their white wings dipped in black binding onto the thorn tree branches.

He lit up a cigarette.

"Ouma Miemie's father buried money over there before the War."

Paul pointed in the direction of the Doorndraai graveyard. It lay lost in the veld that no longer belonged to us. Our land used to stretch to the horizon. Feuds and wills had pulled like a loosening thread, unravelling a blanket of ownership down to the last pocket of Wolwe-fontein.

"Which war?" I sat pulling apart my split ends away from Ma's disapproving gaze.

"Christ, you are ignorant. The Boer War," Paul laughed.

"They dug up the money after the war. Ten pounds. That gave them just enough to start over. Even the English did not stoop so low as to go digging up graves."

"I didn't know that about the English," I said. "I do remember Ouma Miemie saying the years following the Boer War were the happiest years of their lives. When they had nothing." I watched a fish eagle soar from the riverbank. "Why are you so interested in all that family stuff anyway? I find it boring."

Paul stood up. "Your place of origin imprints on you. Writing is a relic of where you find yourself. Of how the seasons manifest. What you call all that family stuff is material to me."

I raised my eyebrows at him.

Oupa Boetie used to say that there was no-one here when the first Trekkers arrived. The black people were wiping each other out. Kimberley created the economy. One could drive down to the diamond fields with a wagon full of fruit and return with enough money to buy a farm. North-facing orange orchards thrived despite the frost. Before the discovery of diamonds, people lived very frugally. The simple Trekker dwelling behind the Wolwefontein house bore testament to leaner times. Pa said we were lucky because the Boer War destroyed many farmers.

Paul took off his clothes. He lit another cigarette. The marks on his forearms were ribbed and white. Like a carelessly sewn seam. The beginnings of solidified scar tissue. He walked naked to the water's edge.

"Provenance, my darling Dominique, is destiny," he said, sinking back into the water as if into an armchair with a cigarette clasped between his lips. "Get your kit off."

"I forgot my swimming costume." Spuytfontein and Blesboklaagte lay beyond the river. Also lost to the family. A Piet-my-vrou sang. Three kolganse flew past.

"Don't be so prissy," he laughed and then dived under the water. A cattle path meandered to the waterline. I folded my clothes next to a porcupine burrow and walked barefoot through the spiky grass stepping over the claw prints of francolins.

Tree trunks turned like giant tumbleweeds in the bloated river's flow. I waded in deeper and Paul pulled me towards him. The current dragged us and then slung us into its vortex. I tried to swim towards the bank but it was futile. Paul held my arms down and shouted, "Stay calm. Just stay calm." The river chucked us onto the other bank much further down and we scrambled onto the sandy verge.

Paul collapsed laughing and held a plastic packet above his head. "In celebration of survival," he shouted and opened the packet to reveal a dry box of cigarettes, matches and a small silver flask.

I wanted to cry. "I don't want to swim back again. I can't. There is no way."

Paul laughed. He took a deep slug from the flask and wiped his mouth with his arm.

"Either we find a farmer on this side of the river to take us back across the bridge," he said, "or we swim back. And we do it soon, because it's getting dark."

"I am not walking to the Geldenhuys's house without clothes."

Paul lit up a cigarette. "Have one," he said. I took a drag from his cigarette and coughed so much I almost threw up. He patted me on the back. "You better have some of this." He pulled the stopper off the silver flask and held it to my lips. The whiskey burnt its way down my throat.

He held the flask in one hand and dragged me into the water. I closed my eyes and clung to him. We were spat out near the southern boundary that Wolwefontein shared with Uitkyk. We ran back along the river's edge, laughing to ward off the cold.

"Careful of the spiders." Paul heaved as we ran, "Pa has not sent slashers down this road for months." Bosveld spiders crocheted blankets of sheer floss between trees and waited in colony formation to trap small birds. We swerved onto a cattle path away from the webs and ran past the carcass pit. Leguaans sometimes gnawed meat off discarded bones the farm people chucked there after slaughtering.

The evening star was delicate and astonishing above the canopy of the truck. Paul picked up some kindling and chucked it onto the back of the bakkie. Sprokkelhout. He switched on the radio and the radiator. I wound the window down and night air flooded into the dusty, trapped heat of the interior. We drove towards the stat beyond the opstal.

"What are you going to do in Johannesburg?" I asked.

"Honest manual labour with these hands," he said keeping his eyes on the road. "I am going to get away from here. Far away."

"Pa said you'll never get a job with your military discharge."

"Is that so?

"Maybe he's right."

"What do you think he knows about the world out there? Seeing it from the perspective of accidentally landed gentry?"

"I was just worried when he said that."

"You should stop worrying about things that don't concern you."

We drove past the collapsing wheat silo and the stone house all locked up and shuttered. The slow-churning windmill pumped water into the cement dam next to the shed. Paul pulled up next to Frans Willem Bouwer's stat. The Bouwers kept the keys for the house and shed. Frans Willem was Pa's foreman. He used to work for Oupa Boetie and Mieta worked in the kitchen with Ouma Koeks. They were Sothos with Afrikaans names. Pa said he had heard, although he doubted it was true, that some of the Transvaal Boers back then had enslaved black women and children. And then they took the family names. Or maybe they renamed themselves for the prestige.

"They are probably asleep already," I said.

Paul knocked softly on the wooden door.

I saw the faint intimation of a lit candle. The door creaked open and Frans stood in the low doorway.

"Evening, Kleinbaas, does Kleinbaas want the keys?"

"No. I came to look at the farm before leaving. I just came to say goodbye."

Frans scratched his chin. "Yes, the veld looks beautiful after the rains."

He shuffled on his feet and coughed a deep, wet cough.

When he stopped coughing he said to Paul, "We're getting old. When is the kleinbaas coming to farm?"

Paul laughed, "First I'm going to look for a wife to bring back. Then I'll come."

Frans Willem said, "Mooi, mooi. That will be good."

Paul took his hand, "Sala hantle ntate."

Frans Willem waved as we drove off.

Nightjars nested in eroded tracks. Paul guided the truck to miss them.

"Maybe you should try and study through Unisa?"

"What for? So they can tell me what to read?"

Paul put his arm around my shoulders and pulled me closer to him.

"You also need a change of scenery. It might help you get over that brainless frat boy you are wasting away over," he said, turning the music down.

"I am not." I blushed in the darkness. I stayed sitting up against him.

Paul whistled the rest of the way home.

Pa was waiting in the driveway.

"I almost called the police. Where the hell have you been? You know bloody well that you are not allowed to take the bakkie without my permission!" Pa was screaming at us through the open window.

"We went to Wolwefontein to swim in the river." Paul's voice was apologetic.

"What? Have you completely lost your mind? Do have any idea how dangerous that is? Don't you know why it's called the False River? Jesus Christ."

Pa grabbed Paul by the collar and forced him out of the driver's seat.

"Don't you ever touch my property again without asking permission, sonny boy, do you understand that?"

"Pa we just went for a ride," he tried to explain.

"Don't talk back to me. I'll donner you off this farm before the night is over. Do you understand?"

CHAPTER 11

I leaned against the wall and closed my eyes. A lone shoe lay on the welcome mat. Morning glory twined around a broken gatepost. Paul's last letter led me to the house in Yeoville. I had left Cape Town before dawn. I had not seen him all year. The Karoo is a journey in repetition. Windpumps. Dry rivers. Limed stones. Pepper trees. I was too tired to leave.

I eventually pushed the door open, mindful of its precarious hinge. Electrical cord and naked bulbs dangled from the ceiling. A navy carpet ran the length of the hallway narrowing to linoleum and a small kitchen. Music drifted from the backyard. A voice came on the radio, announced dedications. Forces Favourites. I heard Paul say, "We must phone in."

I pushed back the gingham curtain in the kitchen and looked. Under a frangipani tree in the backyard a Victorian bath sagged on ball-and-claw feet into an overgrown lawn. Paul was lying in the water reading a newspaper with elbows propped on either side of the curving rim. A cigarette hung from his mouth and a drip hung from the tree. Where the needle entered his skin a small blood rose bloomed.

Dirty dishes and takeaway boxes enveloped the view through the window. A girl was lying on the grass with one arm slung across her eyes and the sleeve on her other arm pushed up to make way for a needle. I had bit the nail on my little finger to the quick. I pushed open the kitchen door and walked out into the garden towards Paul.

"It's the beloved pianist," he said, folding the wet newspaper and throwing it on the grass. He grabbed my hand and kissed it. I pulled away.

"What are you doing?" Flushes burnt up my neck.

He laughed. "Don't be disquieted by this little vignette of depravity. We are just rehydrating after last night's revelry."

"Allow me to present the good doctor from the former East Germany," Paul said, ripping off the duct tape that kept the needle in place. Against the wall a thin, blond man sat smoking with his legs crossed like a woman's. His eyes were watery blue and his nose was large and bent. Ma said there was a category of men who are almost good looking when young. He stood up and walked towards us. The doctor's body odour slammed against me. Sweat, polyester, smoke and brandy. "Now look what we have here. Welcome. We must offer you something." He spoke in a German accent and pointed in the direction of the drips.

"She won't be interested doc," Paul said climbing out of the bath. He stumbled towards me, his long khaki trousers soaked. He put his arm around me and I pushed him away.

"It's just a little opiate, just to take the edge off."

"To take the edge off what?" I stammered.

"The doctor sets aside condemned stock from the university hospital. We prudently put to it to use."

"What do you mean?"

"It gives the good doctor an opportunity to exercise his veining technique. I see it as a community service of sorts," Paul said. "In fact," he continued, "I'm offering my body for the good of society at large. It's positively selfless."

I sat down stiffly under the frangipani tree. I wore a summer dress I had sewn myself – in haste and badly – that did not allow for a proper stride. The dainty floral pattern of black-eyed Susans strained at the seams. The doctor sat down next to me. "Let me help you with that." He bent over my legs, took hold of the seam and offered to rip it up to the middle of my thigh.

The very tall, thin girl in the boots and jersey stood up. She casually ripped the needle out of her arm and stared at the doctor. "Just bugger off you creep, leave her alone." She took languid steps towards the house, came to a standstill before the kitchen door and turned around slowly. "I think we have run out of drugs." A bracelet of tattooed rose stems and buds trailed around her wrist.

"Ja, ja, never fear because I am near." The almost good-looking doctor stood up. He pinched me hard on my arm and said, "Don't go anywhere." I picked up some frangipani blossoms and stacked them on my lap. I crushed the waxy flowers. Their scent was like the expensive soap that Auntie Marina kept in a Delft bowl in the guest bathroom at her farm Evening Star, that one could smell through the thick coloured paper.

I wondered where I was going to sleep. I hated needles so much that I ran six blocks down the Pretoria central business district when I was eight to get away from the dentist. Ma screamed at me all the way home and Pa hit me with a belt, but I still would not open my mouth.

"Tell me about Cape Town. And what's news on the farm?" Paul had climbed back into the bath.

I ignored him.

"You look like a porcelain doll on a rubbish heap," he smiled.

I lay bruised petals in bare patches between the overgrown grass.

"Christiaan is hitchhiking around Germany. He sends one post-card a month with twenty words in accordance with Pa's condition for letting him go. Ma is trying to arrange a scholarship for Firi to go to boarding school. Nadia's Shetland pony kicked Boetie."

Rooms lit up one by one like large box lanterns in the flats next door. The city illumed in counterpoint to the fading glow of sunset. Two men climbed through a hole in the vibracrete that separated the yard from next door. It was Lew and Jonathan.

"Are we going to kap a button or what?" Lew said. He nodded at me and I nodded back at him.

"I must speak to our landlord," Paul said, getting out of the bath again. "We must get this property properly secured to keep out undesirables such as these." He pointed at Lew and Jonathan and laughed.

"Now that I think about it, I wonder who our landlord is?" Paul said, taking off his wet trousers. He took another identical pair off the washing line and put them on.

"Even squatters have rights now, dammit. Wasn't that what the revolution was all about?"

Lew looked at Paul. "You owe my father rent."

Paul smiled at Lew and stuck his hand into the overflowing rubbish bin.

"Lew, you have no sense of occasion."

Paul fished out an empty litre bottle of Coke. He squatted and took the neck of the bottle to the open flame of a cigarette lighter. After turning the bottle a few times, he knocked it against the doorjamb. The neck broke clean, jumping from the body of the bottle like a badly repaired ceramic. Jonathan stuffed it with dagga and a blue tablet he crushed with his heel. They formed a small circle passing the pipe around. Paul took a deep breath and then leant forward, vomiting and drooling into a bucket at the centre.

I took a box of cigarettes lying on the windowsill and went out to the front stoep. I felt weak and sat down. I could make out a tiled floor below the morning glory's pulpy flowers and weak stems. All show and no substance to the plant. A midden squatter to decorate detritus. Ma did not tolerate it in her garden. I wanted to get away from there, but where to go in the dark alone?

I lit up one of the purloined cigarettes and took a deep drag. The street in front of Paul's house was narrow and lined with plane trees. In Cape Town the trees grew in the direction of the prevailing wind. The first time I saw Cape Town, it took my breath away. Paul had sent me some letters. I sent him some money. Half of my allowance once a month. I freewheeled without petrol and only smoked when offered.

The ember of my cigarette glowed in the dark.

I thought about Herman. I only became his girlfriend because he was so persistent. He said he didn't want to live when I said it was over. He moonlighted as an insurance salesman in the coloured townships at night to pay for his business science degree. It depressed him to sell poor people things they didn't need and couldn't afford, and he smoked a lot of dagga to cope with it.

The doctor stood in the doorway and kicked the shoe off the mat.

"I'm on call tonight at the hospital. Shall we go and get something to eat while this lot recover?"

I nodded, stood up and followed him towards the street.

"My car has been impounded. Let's take yours," he said, holding out his hand for my keys.

We drove through the waning remnants of another Jewish diaspora. Late night bookshops, kosher butchers, sheet music vendors and patisseries. "Yeoville is the departure lounge to the new South Africa. Everyone is here. Self-righteous aid workers, angry exiles, drugged refugees from the rich suburbs, young Afrikaners hell-bent on fucking every taboo." He pointed his middle finger up at the sky out of the window. "Beautiful. I love it."

He parked the car outside an empty restaurant. The only lighting came from small candles on the tables. "I don't have any cash. You have to pay," he said, leaning back and lighting up a cigarette.

I checked for the hundred rand Pa had given me as extra for petrol.

"Is there a phone at the house?" I asked.

"I last saw it stored in the oven, it's not really used. The oven or the phone. It's disconnected due to non-payment, but you can make reverse-charge calls. Who do you want to phone, sweetie?"

"I need to phone my parents to tell them I have arrived and I am safe."

He put his hand on my leg below the table and stuck his fingers straight into my crotch.

I jumped up and slapped him.

He laughed and offered me a cigarette. I took one with shaking hands.

The waitress looked at the doctor as if she knew him well. "Yes?" she said sullenly, staring at him. I was very hungry. She took my order without looking at me.

"Two glasses and a bottle of your cheapest wine please," said the doctor trailing his hand up and down the back of her thigh.

The waitress left and he leant over the table.

"I am sure you have a beautiful pussy. I really want to see it." He put his hand back on my thigh, rubbing his palm up and down to below the line of my knickers. He took his other hand and opened my mouth with his fingers.

"Do you have a girlfriend?" I asked, pushing his hand off my thigh.

"Yes, I live with her."

"I thought you lived with Paul."

"She's kicked me out."

The waitress put a plate of soup in front of me. The doctor drank his wine quickly. He kept smiling at me with wine-stained teeth. He smeared butter onto the bread and flecked salt crystals over it.

"Why did you leave East Germany?" I asked.

"It was invaded by West Germany. Colonised. Erased."

He started again with his hand on my dress hem.

"Do you have a boyfriend, sweetie?"

"Yes." I flinched at my lie.

"Why did you come to South Africa?"

He leaned forward. "Where else in the world is a surgeon going to get the chance to sew up so many stab and guns wounds every weekend? If you are lucky, this might happen to you once in your career in Germany. It's a great place to practise trauma."

I finished my soup and set the spoon to the side of the empty bowl.

"Has Paul got a girlfriend?" I asked.

"He's fucking Rachel at the moment. We both fucked her last night at the same time."

I thought about the tall, thin girl and her tattoo of rosebuds. Her wrist so thin and delicate. Her skin so pale. This information given so indiscreetly. I looked down at my hands.

"I could feel your brother's cock, so close when you fuck a woman at the same time. I was in her arsehole. Slick and tight."

I looked up at him. "Do you think she wants just anyone to know this?"

He shrugged.

"Do you think Paul might be gay?"

He almost choked on the slice of bread.

"Man, you are so naive. Christ, where has Paul been hiding you? No sweetie, Paul is not gay. Your brother is interested in every experience available. And every experience available is interested in him."

"Is he a drug addict?"

"What's a drug addict, sweetie?"

"Isn't diagnosis something they teach medical students?"

He laughed. "I think of us as drug users, but abusers? Not yet."

Paul walked into the restaurant with Jonathan. He sat down next to me, his eyes glazed but steady. He took the last slice of bread from the basket and swallowed it.

"I need your car to go on an errand."

Pa said Paul was not allowed to use my car under any circumstances. I looked at the doctor and Jonathan and reluctantly gave Paul the keys.

"The doctor will walk you home. I'll be back in half an hour. I promise." He kissed me on both cheeks.

I paid the bill. The doctor pocketed the tip. We walked uphill away from Rockey Street, past a basement shop full of LPs. He chatted to the thin rasta behind the counter. I waited on the pavement fragranced by a hedge of yesterday-today-and-tomorrow. It was still but for the intermittent ebb and flow of traffic.

At the house he said, "We'll have to sit on the mattress in my bedroom. There won't be furniture in the lounge until the misunderstanding with the landlord is cleared up."

"What misunderstanding?" I asked, standing in the corridor. The air was much cooler after sunset.

"It's too boring to explain. Come here and sit next to me so that I can examine you."

I looked at my watch. Paul had been gone for more than two hours. I sat down on the mattress next to him. He felt my breasts and said, "Take your clothes off."

"These sheets smell really bad," I said pushing his hands off me. He got on top of me and pinned my hands to the side.

"I really want to kiss you," he said. "Do you want me to?"

I did not want him to.

I let him because I did not want to be in the house alone. He leant down and pushed his tongue into my mouth. He tasted of tin. I felt him harden against my thigh. "Can you feel my big cock?" he whispered. "Can you feel, it's so big and hard for you." He pulled my dress up and pushed himself into me. I did not stop him. "Oh baby," he said. "Oh baby you are beautiful. Your beautiful mouth, your beautiful pussy." He pushed my face to the side, grinding up against my neck. A canopy of rustling leaves was discernible in the street lamp's pale glow. I closed my eyes. When it was over he slipped the condom off and chucked it onto the carpet.

"I am on call this evening." He jumped around muttering "fuck" as a refrain under his breath until he had gathered all his things. He called a taxi reverse charges from the telephone inside the oven.

I sat up.

"Paul's been gone for hours now. Do you think something is wrong?" I asked.

"Paul Botha is a prince. Of that I am sure. Something is definitely wrong. Of that I am also sure."

"Please don't go. I don't want to be here alone."

"Don't go and fall in love now," he said pulling the broken door shut behind him.

I waited. I felt afraid. Harrow Road hummed with traffic past midnight and into the early hours. Lights flickered through the windows from passing cars. I got up and opened the door leading into the other bedroom. It was mostly empty but for newspaper Sellotaped against the windows and the smell of unwashed linen. The books on the floor belonged to Paul. Sheets of paper covered in his left-handed scrawl lay scattered among the debris of dirty clothes. I pulled the sheet and pillowcases off his single mattress and chucked them into the bath under the frangipani tree.

Oupa's Olivetti typewriter lay on the floor. I saw a fundraising request from Hilton College. Inside the typewriter was a response addressed to the school bursar. I pulled out the typed page.

Dear Sir, Please immediately desist from sending me these badly phrased begging letters. Should you not have learnt by now to live within your means? In the sincere hope of never hearing from you again, Paul Botha the 6th.

I scrunched the letter up and chucked it in the dustbin. I picked the books off the floor and arranged them in alphabetical order on the south-facing windowsill. I put the notebooks in Oupa's leather suitcase. I packed his clothes in stacks next to the wall. There was no cupboard.

I went to the kitchen and put newspaper on the linoleum tiles. I cleaned the rim of accumulated gunk off the basin and ran the hot tap to wash the dishes. I watered the wilting basil plant underneath the basin. I picked up the shoes and clothes lying discarded down the hallway and pressed the peeling wallpaper back. I took the overflowing rubbish bin and pushed it into the neighbouring property through the hole in the vibracrete wall. I ran back inside and washed my hands and body in the cleaned sink. I swept the hall. I pulled open the caked door of the stove and saw the hearing piece covered in grime. I made a reverse-charges call.

"My liewe Here, child. Dominique, we have been worried sick about you. Why are you only calling now?"

I explained that Paul had taken my car and had not come back.

"This is unforgivable," Pa said, "to leave a young woman alone in a place like that. In this day and age. Make sure you are locked safely in a room. I am on my way."

I sat down in the hallway and listened to the dawn chorus. I lay down against the wall and fell asleep.

I woke with a start. It was Pa, banging the door open. "Good God, what kind of person lives like this?" Pa had come with Goldberg so he could drive my car down to the farm. "Look how he's living. Like a pig, a bloody pig. What kind of person's house is this?"

I looked down, avoiding Pa's gaze. Goldberg stood to the side.

"Goldberg, go and fetch my toolbox." Pa took a screwdriver that Goldberg fetched from the bakkie and mended the hinge, muttering about slapgatte and uitvaagsels.

"Goldberg, you wait in here until that scumbag returns. Then you take the keys of Dominique's car from him, you hear me?"

"I will talk nice with the kleinbaas," Goldberg said.

"You will not exchange a fucking word with that bliksem. Do you understand me, outatjie?"

"Ja baas." His abject demeanour ameliorated Pa's foul mood.

I went and sat in the bakkie. I was glad to leave. Pa felt entitled to drive beyond the speed limit because he was such a good driver. He stopped to refuel and bought a carton of cigarettes. I knew that he was hiding his smoking from Ma. I rolled down the passenger window. I found the constancy of Pa's personal habits comforting. He ate the same breakfast every morning. He liked to have his coffee at eleven and his tea at four. He had a short-back-and-sides hairstyle his entire adult life and weighed the same as he did when he left school.

"I know your brother is smoking dagga."

I thought about the bucket full of saliva and the mandrax. And the needles. "I don't understand it," Pa continued, "when I was young, the bandiete who came round to tar the roads in Bloem were known to smoke dagga. It was something that only criminals did. Apparently girls turn to prostitution to afford their drug habits. To give your body in exchange. Being dead is better than that. Thank God he is at least a man."

Pa lit a new cigarette from the burning end of the last one. "Dagga is a gateway drug. It could lead to something even worse."

"Pa, lots of people smoke dagga. It's even part of some religious rituals."

"Don't you give me that shit. Bloody unbelievable. If any of you other children do this, I will disinherit you immediately."

I waited until he calmed down.

"Is alcohol not a drug?"

"What? Don't talk bloody nonsense to me."

We came home to the familiar air of planting and reaping and narrowing margins. Ma was on her way back from town. Pa wanted the newspaper. Martha gave me a big hug and squeezed my breasts. She said I was too thin. Goldberg phoned to say Paul had come back and that he was on his way. I heard Pa swearing into the receiver.

Pa called me through to the sitting room. We sat on either side of the mahogany chest, waiting for the tea to brew. A tray with a scalloped raised border held the collection of Ma's gleaming brass knick-knacks. A crocodile nut cruncher, two gilded wild swans, a stylised hedgehog.

"At least he is learning a skill. Amazing that he found work with that carpenter. Must be a trial for the old man to have him as an apprentice. But to live like that? With no self-respect?"

I lifted the tea cosy off the pot, casting a glance at Pa. He nodded in assent.

Ma came into the sitting room, breathless, with Boetie, Firi and Cardow in tow. Cardow held his hat in his hand and his blue overall sleeves were rolled up. "Firi, your father has got news for you." Cardow beamed and told Firi that Ma and Pa had managed to arrange a scholarship for Firi. The headmaster of Michaelhouse had just phoned to confirm.

Firi stood there and said "What? What? " Cardow's eyes shone with pride and even Pa's lace agate blue softened. Firi started crying.

"You see," Pa said to Boetie, "what appreciation and respect look like?

"Your grandfather once said to me there is nothing that one would not do for your own children. You will stick your arms elbow deep into shit for them. But, bloody hell, Paul is really trying my patience."

CHAPTER 12

Ma phoned from town. No more district lines for eavesdroppers to share. The new lines rang only for us. Pa sometimes thought a metering click might purport sly ears. He would say, "Surely not? There has to be limits to the stupidity."

Ma was breathless.

"This day will be remembered for ever. Exactly where you were when you heard the news. Like the day America lost Camelot." Ma was in New York when Kennedy was shot, preceded by a lonely year riding the subways on an American Field Service scholarship. "We have waited for this moment for forty-five years." Ma was crying on the end of the line. "For so long they seemed invincible. That it would never be over. I could never have predicted this. Never."

She took a deep breath. "Call everybody. Do it now!"

Ma rushed back from town. Magdaleen and Martha ran upstairs. Pa came storming down from the workshop with Goldberg, Geswind, Likkewaan and Cardow. We all convened in the television room, astonished. Goldberg held a ladder steady while Pa leaned out the window to knock the aerial with a broomstick. Herons nested in the looping tube and bent the image on our television screen out of shape. The Houses of Parliament glowered into view. Nelson Mandela was going to be released. All political prisoners were to be pardoned and set free. Democratic elections would be in the offing. Banning orders revoked. Protests tolerated. Exiles welcomed home. Communal park benches. Seamless beaches. A shared sea.

Magdaleen jumped up and ululated. The men all shook hands like at a prayer meeting and Pa sent Martha to fetch beers for everyone. Nadia sat on Pa's lap plaiting her yellow hair. Boetie and Firi ran outside to revive their cricket game. The skylight panel crackled in the growing heat and a breeze trifled at the bed of blue agapanthus Tietsie had coaxed into flowering.

Likkewaan finished his beer and put the empty bottle onto the tray. "Dankie baas." The other men did the same and then they walked single file back to the workshop on the path past the water tower where Goldberg stopped and threw his cap high up into the air.

Christiaan called from a tickey box in Schleswig-Holstein where he was picking cabbages. Paul phoned from Johannesburg and Ma and Pa forgot to be angry with him.

They sat holding hands and hugged each other. "Our country has been held under water for so long." It was a hot cloudless February Highveld day. The sky open for a whole country to take a deep breath. Many had drowned. Pa thought there might be a rush on canned food at Allem Brothers General Store for stockpiles against Armageddon and the communists. Ma laughed.

"One must give credit to De Klerk," Pa said.

Ma unwound from Pa's arms, "Bullshit."

Ma hated the Nationalists so much, Pa said it was bad for her health. The Erasmus family have weak hearts. "Andries, since I was a little girl I was aware of the injustice when I went to school and our maid's daughter did not. Don't tell me a man like De Klerk had a Damascene epiphany. The truth was there for all to see. I will never credit any of those fucking swine. Never."

Pa said, "Watch you language in front of the children," and Ma said "For Christ's sake" and they went their separate ways and the celebratory tea went cold under the cosy.

Young white men, opinionated and wet behind the ears, began touring the district with a directive to uplift the rural poor and irritate Pa. Field workers. They were missionaries of pleat-making and mayonnaise recipes, gospelling under shed roofs to pliant women in threadbare housecoats. Ma pleaded with them to impart some practical skills but that was not their mandate.

Martha and I taught embroidery to women who came away from the field workers with diplomas in attendance. My malaise came and went. I did not go back to Cape Town. The embroidery was Ma's idea. "At least it's a saleable skill."

"How wonderful to start your own business and create employment," Pa said. He put insulation in the outbuilding so we would not broil in summer or have fingers go rigid with cold in winter.

Paul lost his apprenticeship and set up his own welding shop on the boundary between Alexandra and Marlboro. He had a landline installed and phoned to give us the number and the news of the unreasonable Italian master craftsman. He made metal furniture now and knew shop owners in Johannesburg. He could help to sell the fruits of our handiwork. Metal tables need tablecloths.

I went through Ouma's books in the sunroom. I traced butterflies. Mimicry of mimicry. Wings are scaled like fish and tinted by a serendipitous scattering of light. Colouring arises from a whimsical trick on the eye. Dukes of Burgundy. Painted ladies. Monarchs. I filled rice-paper blotters with outlines of seashells, fleur-de-lys, aloes, damask and water birds. Lavender was popular. We embroidered sheets with blooms as lilac as the fields of Southern France where lavender grew in rundled rows below monasteries. I studied the framed silk herons in Ouma's bedroom at Wolwefontein. Bamboo growing in variegated threads behind thin glass, Mandarin calligraphy gracefully stacked alongside. Magnolia flowers on slender branches and swallows wetting their beaks in a lotus pool. A pagoda temple high amidst snowy pines and satin stich drifting down from the peaks. Handiwork so delicate it could render mist.

Ma helped me with the stitches. Women used to sew up a whole trousseau in the past in preparation for the beds in their husbands' homes. Ma laughed at my two left hands and said, "There is some truth in the wisdom of not learning a skill, because then you are doomed to practise it. To think how many overalls of your father's I have had to adjust in my life." The vocabulary of the craft held the history of its unchanging purpose. Blanket and buttonhole stitch, cross, satin, feather and running stitch. Lappiesgoed in town stocked fabric pens, lining cloth and embroidery hoops. Yarn could be ordered from France in every conjugation of the rainbow. There were twelve skeins apiece in each elegant box, folded in tissue paper, the filaments gathered by a golden label. Wedgwood Blue. Citron Orchard. The company maxim on each skein promised that *from one fine thread a work of art is born.*

Many women came from the squatter camp hopeful for work. Thulanel grew as farming's profit margins shrank and workers were laid off. We counted out threads and hoops and the women brought completed work to the farm at the end of the week. Martha admonished them not to waste the memory thread. They stitched by candlelight and cloth came back from the township reeking of smoke and flecked with blood. Martha ran baths full of hot water to soak the cotton clean and fragrant that would eventually end up gracing spare beds in affluent homes with pruned hedges in faraway cities.

The best embroiderers were the Bouwer women from Wolwefontein. I took work out there once a week when Pa went to check on the cattle. They still built in the old way with mud and dung and charcoal patterning. Elsie Setlotlo's husband regularly punched her in the face and then her eyes swelled shut. She borrowed money against possible future income to continue paying her daughter's school fees. Martha said a man must hit his wife, otherwise she won't behave. Mad Magdaleen disagreed. She said, "Slat terug."

On Saturdays I stood in the queue at First National Bank for coins in ziplock packets to pay exact denominations for piecework. Fifteen cents for a butterfly. One rand fifty for a dragonfly. Lavender cost the most because the buds were formed by tediously spinning a sausage of thread onto the needle and slipping it off into a bullion knot. Martha said the ladies were toyi-toying about that flower so we increased the payment.

Pa bought land at the height of the interest rate and the repayments gnawed at his sleep. The lack of sleep gnawed at his temper. In between planting and reaping, Pa travelled in his bakkie to marches across the Orange Free State as head of the Peace Committee. Oorlog on the peace path. Sometimes I went with him and we wore marshal shirts and Pa warned off young men who tried to talk to me.

Every other week a camera crew arrived from overseas, always asking Pa the same question, "Why don't you support the regime?" They came with expensive equipment and South African cameramen who gave me long, hungry looks over lunch. They left copies of the interviews to be aired in Sweden or Canada on formats that we could not play and the cassettes went into the steel filing cabinet with old school reports. After Rietpan they always went to Koelie Botha who provided racist predictions of doom. Oom Koelie joked to Pa in the co-op that the journalists preferred lunch at his house. Pa referred to him as a jovial cunt. Ma complained that Pa was growing cruder by the year.

A call came from Johannesburg for Ma to join the Women's National Coalition. Ma started driving up and down between the farm and the city, filled with new purpose. Sometimes too opinionated for Pa's liking. She told us how their offices in the Carlton Centre were so high in the sky, the city down below seemed make-believe. In the corridors overtures to traditional leaders were met with dismay. Ritual and custom were euphemisms for oppression.

The field workers were followed by institutes for democracy. Free Staters were sent on exploratory trips into Africa. Ma and Pa went to Zambia on a bus and came back confident. "The drinking buddies found each other in the back of the bus. The Nats and the ANC embraced each other over bottles of whiskey like young lovers," Pa said, "but my liewe Here, just don't ask about the state of the so-called 'collective farms' up there. Hopefully reality will cure the ANC quickly of such childish fantasies."

Then a Polish immigrant shot Chris Hani with a borrowed pistol. Nerves frayed and goodwill threatened to unravel in the wind. Pa held a memorial service in the Waaisand school hall and still the old men held their hands down when the young ones saluted and shouted "viva". Nelson Mandela sent a falcon into the widening gyre. Some old lizards took fright and stirred. A date was finally set for the national elections.

Boetie's birthday was coming up. Boetie played prop in the under-eight team and they called him Os. He wanted a rugby match at his party and Paul as coach, because Paul had been first-team centre at Hilton and was often man of the match. Boetie grew fatter and fatter in front of the television with the remote in his hands and condensed-milk cans under the cushions. Paul used to sit on Boetie's face when he wanted the remote. Sometimes just to pass wind.

Phone calls were made. Paul found an old school friend who had a car and they would come for the weekend. I went to town and bought vleispasteitjies and koeksisters. Paul liked to dip frozen koeksisters in his coffee. Pa put beers in the fridge. Rain was unequivocally on its way.

I had been sitting on the stoep, watching a cloudbank roll in from the west. The oncoming storm chased butterflies from the remembrance bush that flourished by the rubbish dump. Flying ants stumbled into flight at the beginning of the season as clumsy harbingers of rain. Occasionally, locust plagues resulted in keratin bodies exploding in green and yellow onto dashboards. Razed crops had to be retrieved in insurance offices.

I went into the kitchen to tell Ma about the butterflies with bruised wings taking refuge under the wisteria trellis. Pa was talking excitedly to Ma. Terror Lekota had phoned and wanted to talk to Pa. He could not hear very clearly because of the static on the line. Ma was roasting a leg of lamb. The fatted calf. The line went bad, then died. All cabling becomes conduit for static when an electrical storm sweeps in. Pa shouted to make himself heard over the din on the roof, "Thank God all our vehicles are parked away. I pity the damn kid that is driving Paul here. There is no escaping this kind of damage." Hail covered the lawn in a blanket of ice that emulated snow. When the clouds pulled clear, fog would drift from the ice. Pa always promised that if it snowed in Jerusalem we would see snow in our next winter. It had not snowed in the Holy City for forty years, but Nadia and Boetie lived in hope. I heard wheels rumble over the cattle grid and saw splintered headlights through the dark and rain. I turned away from the window, where storm water sluiced down the panes. They came rushing in through the happy door. The friend who had brought Paul was Adi. I remembered him from Pietermartizburg.

"I know you."

We stood looking at each other across the room.

"I know you too."

Paul made introductions and the dogs barked and the storm raged and the children ran and food was brought to the table amidst scuffling chairs and clanging warming drawers and clattering plates. Sweetened pumpkin. Marog from where it grew wild by the orchard. Kidneys in cream on an oval pewter tray.

Paul picked at the leg of lamb while Ma was carving. She slapped him and said, "Look at your disgusting fingernails." Pa took her by the arm, "Easy now, Sandra, calm down."

I looked at Adi and blushed. It was raining so loudly I could barely hear what he was saying.

"This is what I missed when I was at university in England," he said.

"Doesn't it rain there all the time?" I asked.

"Not like this."

Pa called us to the table. Boetie, Firi and Nadia sat in a row staring at Adi. Adi sat next to me and held my hand while Pa said grace. I glanced at my drawing book on the shelf behind the table. I had sketched songbirds in cages as an embroidery motif. Some cages were open and the birds had hopped out onto branches. Pastel leaves fluttered down the page. "Segen Here wat wij eten, laat ons nimmer Uwe Naam vergeten. Om Godswil. Amen." Pa coughed to clear his throat and spat the phlegm into a handkerchief.

Ma said, "That's revolting Andries." Pa ignored her.

"Enthoven. I remember that name from United Party days. Is that your family?"

"Yes, Mr Botha. They live in London now Mr Botha."

Adi had dark blond curly hair, milky skin and eyes that were undecided between blue and green. He had broad shoulders and a burdened conscience. I could see Pa made him nervous.

"Did you finish your studies?" Ma asked, looking at Paul.

"I studied politics, philosophy and economics. I graduated a week ago."

"Adi's call came fortuitously," Paul said. "I know he has always taken a keen interest in rural upliftment." Paul looked at me and winked.

"I've come back because I want to make a meaningful contribution to change. In England I felt disconnected."

Pa said to Adi that he came across as an exemplary rooinek. Pa liked speaking Afrikaans to English-speaking people.

"Adi, your civic-mindedness calls for a celebration," Paul said, pulling me closer. "Take us out for a drink."

We were excused from the table and Ma sent the children to their room. Pa called me upstairs. "You can go with them. He looks decent, unlike the other riffraff your brother consorts with."

We took Adi's car into town, to the Mahem Hotel. It was boarded up. There were no longer enough travelling salesmen to warrant its operations. Quartz tiles on the walls and modernist balustrades below the awning hinted at a once-expectant aesthetic grown forlorn in chipped cement. The bar still traded profitably.

Paul went to buy drinks. He came back with four beers and a glass of wine. I looked at his armful of alcohol. "I don't drink beer." He pulled his chair out and put the wine down in front of me. "One beer is for Adi, the other three for me."

"Is your family still running the economy?" Paul asked Adi as he downed his first quart. "Not exactly. They never did," Adi laughed.

Paul lit up a cigarette and looked at me. "A rare man this. He stems from the northern suburbs full of tragically misguided Albions inflated with a sense of self-importance. On the whole obscenely stupid and morally bankrupt. He is the exception who proves the rule. Welcome home."

Adi shuffled in his seat. "And you, Paul? What are your plans?"

Paul laughed. "I am within reach of my emigration fantasies." He gave us a conspiratorial smile. "I have an epistolary in my suitcase and a library in my head. I read and write the way Boetie eats, without discrimination. That will be my passport out of this wasteland."

Paul's eyes had dark rings under them. He walked up to the counter and ordered more drinks.

"What work do you do?" I asked Adi. I steadied myself against the swaying table.

"I work for the Metropolitan Chamber in Johannesburg. We're trying to integrate local government services between the apartheid councils and township civic structures."

I was impressed.

Paul called Adi over for a game of pool.

One of the drunks playing against them called Gert brought me a drink. He stood next to me with bloodshot eyes, his dark hair greasy and framed with rivulets of sweat. He looked vaguely familiar. He may have been in Christiaan's class in primary school. I was the only girl in the bar.

Gert stood closer. "I am fighting to protect white South Africa. Women and children." I ignored him.

He leaned over and whispered in my ear, "There is an ANC farmer in this district."

"Really?" I said. "I doubt that."

"It's true," he slurred. "And we are going to kill him. I was in his house already. It's Andries Botha from Rietpan."

I stood up. "For your information he is not ANC. And he is my father."

I went up to Paul and whispered into his ear that these men wanted to kill Pa. Paul just laughed. "I want to kill him too."

"Paul, I think we should go."

Paul pulled me closer with the cigarette hanging out of his mouth.

"Sliminique, that special class piece of trash mechanic appie can't even hit a pool cue, which is what he was genetically engineered for. It's a pick-up line, original I will grant him, but certainly no threat. He's just a harmless barfly."

Paul said, "Gert come back to the pool table. Let's square up for a new game."

I went back to the table and sat down. Adi fiddled with his pool cue while Paul stacked the balls on the billiard table. I left the apprentice assassin's offering untouched. I saw umbrellas being folded up in the lobby and three black men walked into the bar. They went over to the counter and sat down on the stools. The barlady did not discriminate in her indifference. Gert muttered that he did not drink with kaffirs. Paul stuck out his pool cue and stopped Gert moving towards them. Adi looked at me and gestured at the door.

"Be cool, Gert," Paul said, "we are going to finish this game and the loser is buying a drink for everyone in this bar. And I mean everyone." Eventually he nodded in sullen assent. Paul sunk all the balls with a cigarette hanging from his mouth and pointed at the bar with his pool cue. "Go on Gertjie, you look like a man of your word."

Gert went to the counter and reluctantly ordered a round. Adi came and sat down next to me, his arm resting on the back of my chair. The three black men raised their beers at us. They were municipal officials from Kroonstad.

"One must try to be gracious in victory," Paul said, dancing towards the table with more cans, "but it's so hard."

"I want to go home, Paul." Adi agreed. Paul took the beers with him in the car.

"One must never fear a fight, though," Paul said. "I read somewhere that there is nothing more life-affirming than having the shit kicked out of you in a bar."

Adi drove and Paul rolled a joint in the passenger seat. He flipped open the sun shield for light and fished out the dagga seeds. He was expert at the task and the only taker. "Why are you taking the seeds out?" Adi asked.

"Are you serious, broer? Have you never rolled a joint?"

Adi said he hated smoke.

Paul rolled down the window and chucked the seeds out. "The seeds make you sterile. I would not want to deprive the gene pool of my swell contribution." He lit up the joint. "They can bliksem me all they like," he said, "in fact I would welcome it."

I showed Adi the turn-off to the farm. It was easy to lose your bearings in the platteland at night.

Paul sighed, "I'm already in the mood to get back to Johannesburg. I'm missing my kaffertjies who work for me."

I could see Adi was shocked. "Paul, you can't use that word," I said. "It's not funny."

"For God's sake Dominique, I have been a communist for twenty years. I have earned the right to use the word kaffir."

Paul's eyes were bloodshot. "We must stop this absurd simplification of each other. It's boring. Let the struggle in this respect not continue."

In the morning Adi helped me to put cake and popcorn out under the trees while Ma fetched Boetie's school friends in town. Pa was meant to prepare the field next to the dam for the rugby match. He and Ma had a fight about it in the morning and Pa said he was too busy for this kind of rubbish. When Pa walked out the kitchen, Ma said, "You see? You see? Always just promises." Paul took the slasher and made a rugby field in the paddock. Firi brought the seven requested black boys from the stat. None of them had ever played rugby. When Boetie heard that Adi played for his university team, he chose him as coach over Paul. Also, Adi did not smoke. Boetie and Nadia used to crush Paul's cigarettes. They did not want him to smoke because it was bad for his health.

"Cool," Paul said. "My team are the All Blacks. Boetie is the birthday boy captain of the whities. Firi, you are the captain of the darkies." Paul took his barefoot team aside and gave them a rudimentary explanation of the game. The white boys had their rugby jerseys and togs on. They complained about it being too hot. They complained that there were too many thorns. They complained that it was not fair.

"You are wearing shoes, you little faggots," Paul laughed at them and Adi scratched his head and smiled. Nadia came cantering through the avenue of blue gums. She climbed off her horse and onto Paul's shoulders. He carried her up and down the try line, shouting instructions at his team. "Kill those little boere," Paul shouted. "Eat them like mielies."

At half-time Boeddens and Jan van der Spuy wanted to swop coaches.

The All Blacks won fifty nil. Boetie cried.

Pa came home from the workshop at the end of the day and we all climbed onto the bakkie and drove out to the furthest field. A pot was boiling on a small fire in the wenakker. We picked green maize and broke off the silken threads before putting them in the pot. Ma brought butter and salt and we ate the soft white pips in the setting sun. "Koningskos," Pa said, food fit for a king. Adi sat next to me. He and Paul were leaving after the meal. He asked if he could come and see me again. Paul wanted Pa to lend him money to help grow his welding business. Ma said they would think about it.

Ma said afterwards you could see that Adi had been properly educated, unlike Paul's raw intelligence that just slid into caustic wit. "Snide remarks," Ma called his utterances. She noted me carefully paying attention. Adi wrote a thank you letter to Ma and Pa. He spelt finish with two n's. I blushed when I read that. I waited and embroidered. Ma wrote a letter to Paul and asked me to take it to the post office when I fetched threads sent in bulk from France.

I opened the envelope.

Dear Paul,
After our recent conversation, I have very sadly reached the conclusion that all your work and effort has for the most part been to enrich various drug dealers. Since I have no wish to do the same, we are structuring our business so that no proceeds of our own efforts can ever be employed in the same manner. You remain, as always, our beloved child and welcome in our house when you behave in a way we find acceptable. Persistent abuse of yourself and lack of provision for your independence and future is not.

I folded the letter back into the envelope. The stamp had a picture of a wattled crane drawn by an artist called Dennis Murphy.

Terror Lekota came to visit Pa every weekend to watch Free State play rugby. Pa called him Tronkvogel because he spent so many years in jail for being a terrorist. When Terror saw the braks that Eunice gave us, he wanted one. Pa said, "You can't be serious." Terror was adamant. Pa said, "In that case, please feel free to relieve me of one of these damned things." Boetie tried to catch the white dog for Terror and almost killed it by dropping the sofa on its head. Terror christened his dog Botha and the dog immediately rose in Pa's estimation. Pa said, "That is the best one of the lot, the one you chose."

"Kom Bothatjie," Terror whistled. He held the dog on his lap while they screamed, "Pale toe Vrystaat!"

"Go fetch us some biltong," Pa said. I went to the freezer. It was packed full of meat marked by date with a black Koki on masking tape. One year Ouma Koeks went away for a month and the electricity tripped in her kitchen. A whole carcass defrosted, then rotted and swelled with maggots. The kitchen floor had to be chopped and relaid because of the indelible stench. After Ouma Koeks died, Tannie Zelma came and some of the furniture were removed. Pa kept saying he was still going to get it all back from her and restore the empty, shuttered house at Wolwefontein to what it was in his mother's day.

"Oliver Tambo is coming to the Free State next week. Can he come and sleep here?" Terror asked, feeding Bothatjie some biltong. "In God's name, Tronkvogel, don't waste such good meat on that runt." Terror laughed at Pa. Ma's biltong was delicious, even when frozen. Pa shaved it in very thin slices, so it warmed to the touch. She used the best cuts and removed all the fat. "Yes, of course. It goes without saying," Pa said. "It would be a great honour for our family." After the rugby Pa and Terror went to the swimming pool. Pa was teaching Terror to swim with Boetie's waterwings.

I told Adi about the visit. We were not allowed to say anything about Tambo sleeping over because people from the township might swarm to the farm. Adi brought me a box of peaches in individual purple paper wrapping and a rose bush in soil and black plastic. I knew he got it from the stall under the Casuarina trees just outside Parys. The same traders had been selling there for years, alongside an old omie who sold veldskoene from a Venter-waentjie, where Pa bought all his shoes.

They came with many advisors. Terror brought Bothatjie along. The dog was transformed. Bothatjie had a long, glossy coat and a ribbon in his hair. Ma and Martha cooked a special dinner. The house was lit up with candles. She put napkins in serviette rings and made grissini like in Italian restaurants. Ma worried hers were not as nice as the ones you could buy. Pa said she was being vol fiemies about the food, but Ma said they would be used to all sorts of exotic food from overseas. Ma always got nervous about entertaining guests.

Oliver Tambo was tired. He was too tired to eat dinner. They helped him to the spare room with the Morris wallpaper and a vase filled with roses from Auntie Marina's garden. He sat on the brass bed and told Pa that he had missed eating pap all those years in England. Pa told him how he gets the Allems to grind growwe pap for him especially, not this refined nonsense stripped of all goodness that you buy in the supermarket. "I will arrange to have some specially milled for him, and send it up to Sodom and Gomorrah with Dominique," Pa said. I was going to university in Johannesburg.

One of Mr Tambo's advisors wore a navy blazer with gold buttons, cuff links and a pink shirt, and he spoke for hours while we sat below the wisteria under the stars. Ma said in the kitchen, "That man is a true diplomat." Adi talked to him at length. He understood constitutional issues and had been at the Dakar talks. Mosquitos drowned in the citronella candles. The din of frogs gradually let up as the night grew colder. The diplomat hoped to go back to New York. "After all these years in exile, South Africa is no longer for me," he said. His deep voice had the timbre of resignation. He came from a township outside Bloemfontein and could speak Russian fluently.

"Imagine that," Pa said, "Russian." Whiskey and ice clinked around the table.

The next morning Pa asked Oliver Tambo if he could drive him through the stat, as a wonderful surprise for the farm people. Tambo agreed and we went in my new CitiGolf. The station wagon was in for a service and the bakkie had too few seats. Cardow dropped his hoe and ran after the car. "A great man," he shouted, "a great man." People ululated and Oliver held out his hand through the opened window. Pa drove slowly. I sat in the back with Adi. He took my hand and held it for the whole journey.

Ma and Pa were offered places on the ANC electoral list. Pa said he must remain loyal to the party he had supported all his life. And the party that his father had supported before him. Ma wavered. She decided to follow Pa in his decision. It was the price she always thought she had to pay for peace. That night Adi told me about Berkeley, Locke and Hume. I was impressed.

Adi lived in a cottage on a farm just outside Johannesburg. There were blue gums and frost and lightning strikes. Adi kept two lovebirds called Ethelrood and Selwyn and a snake he fed with frogs from a pond in the garden. His family used to live in the beautiful thatched house with casement windows and yellow silk curtains. There was a library full of first edition books and filled with important furniture and pictures. Oil paintings like Ma's copies, except these were real. I thought they should be in a museum open to the public. Adi understood the nuts and bolts of transition and structures. He worked on dismantling the legacy of apartheid in the biggest office building in the southern hemisphere, a sarcophagus on Braamfontein hill conceived to administer separate development. Adi was religious. He described his political and spiritual awakening when a priest called Caesar Molebatsi came to Michaelhouse and roused him from privileged slumber. Pa did not have to worry about us being together like man and wife.

I had found a cottage at the end of an avenue of blue gums next to a sports field in Melville. Ma would come and go when she spent time in the city working for the Women's National Coalition. I did not really want to live with Ma. I took the growwe pap and a box of vegetables from Ma's garden and even some eggs to the Tambos' house. They had a white housekeeper who would not let me inside. "Just repeat again who you are. Leave it in front of the gate," she said. The driveway was long and I had to shout. "It's vegetables and maize meal from Andries Botha's farm, from Viljoenskroon!" Eventually Oliver Tambo's son came outside and thanked me in a British accent.

Ma arranged for a Bulgarian guitarist to play a concert in the entrance hall at Rietpan. After the Berlin Wall came down, musicians from Eastern Europe flooded across the map and into the small towns in the Free State. He played a galloping horse with his fingers on the wood until the horse ran over the imaginary hill of the body of the guitar. Everyone sat dead still on the teak staircase until it snapped and we all applauded.

I decided to take up the guitar and found a teacher with a long red beard that he suffused in Gauloises smoke. Guitar strings came wound in a circle in paper packets decorated in calligraphy. "The strings of the higher chords are made from gut. These sounds come literally wrenched from a body. You are locked in dance with your guitar. It is second only to the voice, which is the instrument that comes straight from God." The fingernails on his right hand were kept long for plucking and between chords he moaned about being broke.

I did not like the city. I was listless at university and my marks bore witness. I was meant to report on Paul's progress. I visited Paul at his workshop in Alexandra on Friday afternoons. Despite Ma's protestations, Pa lent him the money with lots of conditions and strings attached. The strings were coming loose at one end. His workers would knock off early. The workshop was a long shed that opened onto a scrapyard at the back, and the front door faced onto Alexandra. When Paul had money, he spent it. He bought cake and Italian filter coffee and we sat watching the Zulu impis coming up the road. "The war across the street," Paul called it.

"Ma is doing well at the Women's National Coalition. They want to give her a full-time job."

"Beats Tupperware parties," Paul said. He was done welding for the day and rolled a joint. "How is Christiaan?"

"He is coming back at the end of the month. He is going to work for Pa."

"Good luck to him."

I went into the toilet. A lime scale artery grew below a leaking tap and little silver tinfoil packets lay strewn on the basin. A broken shard of mirror was stuck to the wall with double-sided tape. Outside, milk-soft butterflies sat on a bush of thistle weed in the pining light of late afternoon.

Paul had taken a book out of my bag. "Are you reading this?" he asked.

I sat down again and laughed. "Our lecturer keeps reminding the class we could have no conception of the setting because we all come from Benoni."

"Stupid cunt," Paul said, blowing out a deep drag from his joint. "If Evelyn Waugh himself did not come from a proverbial Benoni he could never have written *Brideshead Revisited* with such inflamed ambivalence and covetousness. There is so much value in being a liminal person. Especially here where so many distinct historical and linguistic fantasies are imprinted on the same physical space. That is the pain and the privilege of the outsider perspective. You see these worlds clash up against each other and shatter and jostle for primacy." Paul's eyes were bloodshot from the dagga.

"Paul, I don't think you are living the right kind of life."

"Dom, with all due respect, what do you think you know about life? I have fucked more men than you have."

His nails were grimy but his hands had the raw red colour of labourers' hands washed with strong soap. There was evidence of effort.

"You look nice, by the way," he said to me. "Have you finally fallen out of love with the idea of being sick?"

I started packing my things away.

"The doctor wants to see you again. Can I give him your number?"

"No. Tell him I said don't go falling in love."

Paul laughed.

"I am with Adi now."

Paul sucked hard on his cigarette. "That's better. Adi is a barefoot man of God."

He looked at me. "I'm cleaning up my act. I'm tired at the end of the week. I sweat for the rent I pay. I make an honest living. Why the fuck does the guilt trip get pulled on me, always? It's the fucking gold standard of our family interaction. It's so easy to fall outside the category of acceptability with them. Judged as being rotten. It's a hell of a thing to condemn your own child. I reject it. I reject it with the contempt that it deserves." He shifted around. "Ma's sight is restrictive. It results in a strangled portrait. Can you lend me R200? Monastic and coy sister of mine?"

Adi and I went down to the farm on weekends. I handed out embroidery work on Saturday mornings and he went round and round the dam in his canoe. On Mondays he dropped me off at the Melville cottage and went to work.

I unlocked the gate and walked down the flagstone steps to the cottage. The trellis door was open. Strange. I turned the knob on the door, and it slid open. I walked inside. The fridge door was open. My wardrobe had been emptied onto the carpet. My guitar and CD player were gone. There was no longer a television in the sitting room. I walked to the stove. It was on. Someone had made Italian filter coffee. And smoked cigarettes. Two used coffee cups. I sat down and phoned Adi's office. The phone just rang. He would already be in a chamber meeting. I phoned Paul's workshop. The phone just rang. When the police came, I showed them the cups for fingerprints. They just laughed at me and made a case number so that I could claim from insurance.

I went to look for Paul in Alexandra. Zulu impis were marching up the road. Josias, one of the three men working for Paul was pulling the security door shut in a rush. I rolled down the window. "Josias, where is Paul?"

He pointed at the impis. "You must leave now, quickly. Paul got sick. He had to go to hospital."

"To hospital? What's wrong with him?"

"He got bronchitis. But he is back at home now. Please Ma'am, you must not stay, there is going to be trouble."

I turned around and drove to Paul's house. Paul had moved in with an older man in Yeoville. Into a corner house near Rockey Street. I stopped at the Spar and bought butternuts, onions and curry to make soup. Some dark chocolate. The security gate was a welded Escher diagram of birds repeating themselves. I had seen the templates in Paul's workshop. I rang the bell. I looked down the street. I did not feel safe here. Footsteps came down the hall and the door with the stained-glass fanlight was opened by a soft-spoken man with dark-blond hair in his late forties.

"You must be Paul's sister," he said in a whisper.

"Are you Mark?" I asked. He turned around and beckoned for me to follow him. I walked down the long hall to the far end that opened into a large bedroom. There was a mattress on the floor and Paul lay sleeping. He was very pale and breathing heavily.

I sat down next to Paul and turned to Mark. "Why does he need a drip for a lung complaint?"

The walls were covered in pencil drawings of a man behind bars with his flesh peeling away.

I started crying. "I got robbed. My guitar was stolen."

Mark said, "Let me get you some tea, darling."

He came back and handed me a mug. He sat down in an armchair, the only other piece of furniture in the room. He lit up a cigarette. I drank the tea. John Cage was playing softly on the stereo. Mark seemed to be what Pa would call a refined person.

"Where are you from?" I asked softly. "You sound English."

"London originally, but I would have called New York home, if it was not for my four years in a New Mexican jail. Now it's all about new beginnings. The new South Africa seems like a good place for a personal reinvention project."

"In jail for what?" I spoke too loudly.

"I took the rap on a heroin bust for a good-looking boyfriend bastard dealer. It had nothing to do with me. He stashed his gear in my flat in Manhattan. After I got out, he gave me this house for my grand gesture." He gestured around bitterly. I wondered if Paul was sleeping with Mark.

"Are those your drawings?" I asked. "They are so good."

He shrugged his shoulders. "Doing time gave scope for practice."

He finished his cigarette and stubbed it into an overflowing ashtray.

"Your brother OD'd. There is nothing wrong with his lungs."

"What does OD mean?"

Mark laughed. "Ask that foolish boy himself, he is awake now." Then he got up and left the room. Paul put his hand out and I held it.

"I overdosed on pinks. Wellconal."

The branches of a peach tree were ticking up against the burglar bars outside the window.

"Before I went on a binge I phoned home and spoke to Nadia. Just to be reminded of what is pure and true. I imagined her in the hallway in her little school uniform. Her voice, when she recognised mine, almost split my heart. I need to get away from here. To get away from the drugs. I think I should move to Cape Town."

"We should phone Ma and Pa. There are places where you can get help. We can find out about them. I don't want you to go."

He managed a wry smile. "A hospital for addicts. Without even a single movie star for atmosphere."

CHAPTER 13

"We are entangled," Adi said kissing my fingers. "The first time I saw you when you were fourteen I knew we would be together. Nothing will change, you'll see. Don't cry any more."

I lay with my head on his chest next to the dead tree where the vlei spilt over into the pan, listening to the comforting lilt of a heart at its high-water mark. The soft imprint behind his neck a last vestige of boyhood. His back slung with sinew and muscle that heaved him gently over me in his want. The news of him leaving for England stung the fading day.

Somewhere in the eragrostis grass, mice and shrews lurked. Like thoughts. Like secrets. An owl sat in the forking branch of a dead gum. Watching. The first faint cluster of stars gathered like a shy family of itinerants. Flayed leaves were castanets in the wind's distemper. Venus drew up along a sash, burning a firebreak against sunset. Tilting, decanting the day.

Adi left after the vote came in.

In cities maps were rolled open on suffrage within walking distance and blue thumbtacks marked democracy at its point of entry, like light leaking into a tomb. I worked at the voting station near Blesboklaagte on the road between Kroonstad and Bothaville. A lane of sisal trees led to the abandoned district store covered in wrinkling paint and open rafters gone mealy with worm. I inked fingernails from a counter that once sold blankets, snuff and sugar. When there were still half cents and half loaves. People queued for hours in the sun. Cripples, the very old, men in blue overalls, women in threadbare housecoats, Ma voting for the first time, occasionally a farmer and his worried wife. Was this the mark of the beast?

After the queues let up, I sat under a tree with an old black policeman. Morné Swart sat many ranks ahead of him in the police vehicle in the shade of a seringa tree. Morné was in my year at school. The black man always passed over. "Now I am too old for promotion," he said bitterly. At nine that night, we watched the filled boxes sealed and taken to the church hall in Kroonstad. I drove with Pa in his bakkie. I was counting votes and he was an official observer.

Pa walked up and down, admiring the sandstone, woodwork and the monument to men who died in the Boer War. A clock tower showed time with golden arms and ships sailed on stained-glass waves below a roof painted olive. Incongruous, tumid rooftops hinted at the onion domes of Russia, impossibly far away.

Each ballot paper was folded open and double checked along a row of vested interests. I counted but saw nothing that would send Pa to parliament or the Volksraad. Our neighbour Faan Senekal came over. "Andries, for all these years we have been misled by our own people. They sold us down the river. I apologise for my own blindness. Now I am with you and Sandra." Pa kept repeating that on the drive home in the dark. The windows open, the cool air, smoking. "Now I am with you and Sandra. My magtig." Ma was in Bloemfontein watching the vote come in. "The Democratic Party should never have stood in the Free State. Oh well, that's it then. I have done my bit," Pa said. "I must concentrate on farming now."

Christiaan went out to the lands early and came back late. He hardly spoke, apart from the rare occasion when he was very drunk. In the evenings he painted Picasso and Matisse impressions onto the back of poster boards in his bedroom. Ma said to me, "I have been stuck on this farm for thirty-five years. Go to Cape Town. There is nothing here for you."

Paul was now a welder in Cape Town, building film sets. He worked in a large shed on an isthmus where long ago the Dutch kept horses. Streets turned inland, away from the windblown sea with names like Lowestoft, Canterbury and Shakespeare. He sent letters to Ma and Pa. They worked longs hours and often went into the Karoo. Things were better there, Paul wrote. The solitude and emptiness were purging. Pa thought that sounded very promising.

I packed my bags and Pa bought me an aeroplane ticket. I took two kittens along for company. Trompie and Saartjie were the sole survivors of a litter preyed upon by a wildcat that snuck into the laundry and bit off one kitten's head each night. After hours of waiting in the darkened passage with his gun, Pa gave up and said, "Let the damned cats sleep in your room then." The wildcat was sly, his motives enigmatic.

They did not like the idea of me staying with Paul. Two stints in rehab in two years. It was only till I could find my own place. The last time he had come to Plettenberg Bay, he'd slept in the public toilets near Lookout Beach. Pa and Ma were mortified. Paul laughed. "I am not some kind of tramp sleeping in a car, this is en suite accommodation." Eunice walked over and took his dirty clothes and returned them washed and ironed in a Checkers packet.

Oupa Bob came to Ma and Pa pleading, "Don't be too harsh on him."

Dr Kriel gave me blue pills to wrap in polony and feed to Trompie and Saartjie before the flight. I sat by the window as the plane banked away from the rampant green of the Highveld summer. His veterinary practice was next to the cattle enclosures at the showground that was steadily going to seed. Pa had never liked Dr Kriel because he thought he knew more about cattle than Pa did. Ma once brought Dr Kriel a giant heron with an injured leg. He set the leg and we freed the bird back into the vlei. Ma kept the veterinary invoice for its curiosity value. Far down below we passed over Wolwefontein. In years gone by, Oupa Boetie used to set his clock to it for the evening's first drink. "The Boeing has passed over head." Lush clouds thinned to wisps over the Karoo. Life blushed in sporadic clefts of remembered river. Lonely farms were strung along dry stony beds. We flew over wheat fields, mountains, vineyards and across False Bay, crimped into foaming pleats by the wind.

Trompie and Saartjie came onto the carousel fast asleep in a plaited rush picnic basket with enamelled seams. Paul fetched me from the airport in his work bakkie. We drove into the wind, past cooling towers and through the smell of sewage, trees growing skew and sparse in a bleak sprawl, towards the setting sun fastening a vermillion braid onto the backlit mountain.

Paul rented a room in a house on Somerset Road with a frangipani tree in the garden. Flowers lay like fragrant scrap on the overgrown lawn. "I've lost the keys," he said. Prostitutes congregating at the robots smiled and waved at Paul. "Do you know them?" I asked.

"The night shift." He tried to open the lock with a bank card.

"Is it legal for them to be seen like that?"

"One of them took a lead pipe and smacked out a previous tenant's front teeth. They are rough. I let them use our toilet. Only the ones I know."

He managed to push the lock open. "Won't that destroy your card?" I asked.

"There is nothing in that account to be retrieved."

The doorway opened onto a steep staircase and a fitted carpet creeping up to the dado with hundreds of Polaroids stuck to the wall with Prestik. "They belong to the housemate," he said and carried my suitcase into his room. "He's harmless."

I opened the picnic box. Trompie and Saartjie stood up groggily. I put them on the carpet and they collapsed again into sleep. Paul laughed. "I want what they are on." I went to get them some water where, at the back of the house, the passageway widened into a small kitchen with linoleum tiles and a wooden table. Paul came through with a bottle of whiskey and some canned olives.

"I've taken out some of your corny music to play," he said, wriggling through the boxed window above the toilet. "We are climbing onto the roof to look at the mountain." He hung down into view with a lit cigarette in his mouth. "Pass me the bag." I gave him the rucksack and followed through the window. I climbed up a drainpipe using its bolts as footholds. "Jesus, Paul," I shouted, "I can't come back this way."

"You won't need to," he laughed, "it's too dangerous."

He gave me a hand and pulled me up onto the roof. "Only walk on the joints where the roof sheets lie on the trusses." The tired iron groaned beneath our feet. Doves shuffled along roof spines, making way. Paul's house was the bookend of a long row of dishevelled Victorians. Traffic hummed below the jumbled roofscapes. Paul unscrewed the whiskey and handed me the bottle. We drank in turn. A cold sea rushed up against its beaches with shredded forests of kelp salting the air. Table Mountain held a lustrous scarf of twilight city to her throat. Clouds pulled into jade crevices.

Paul put on my collection of arias. A muezzin called from the Bo-Kaap in antiphonal drift on the wind. A profaned motet.

"Sjoe Paul, it's beautiful."

"Nothing like Wolwefontein," he said.

We drank more. He wanted news of everyone. I kept to myself the disinheritance Christiaan and I had had to sign. To farm on Wolwefontein one day was always Paul's dream. There he was going to write books like Le Roux did on Koffiefontein, only better.

"Firi made the rugby team at Michaelhouse."

"I'll go and watch his first match. I promised him that." Paul leant back flush against the sloping roof.

"This music is breaking my heart." Then he started telling me about Dudu. She had left for Europe the month before I arrived. Paul had always had women. Many. Never one he spoke about like this. "She is a little priss pussy, just like you. I am going to fetch her. I just need to clean up my act first." He took a deep swig and wiped his mouth with his arm. "That is her prosaically stated condition."

I poured more whiskey and laughed. "Ma's heart is still irregular. Oorlog is fighting. What can I say?" Ma felt bitter towards Paul. But then he knew that. We slid back slowly and drunk through Paul's window into safety. "Let's go and swim."

"I don't want to leave the cats alone yet."

"We will be quick," he said, dragging me down the stairs, the bottle of whiskey in hand. Paul lived close to the beach where Ingrid Jonker had drowned. Ouma Celia treasured a typed folio of poems that Ingrid Jonker gave her one drunken night fifty years ago in Rooi-Els. Ma remembers hiding behind the sofa with her brother while Oupa Bob recited the *Rubáiyát* of Omar Khayyám at the top of his voice and Ouma and Ingrid danced the tango up and down the hallway of the guesthouse. Paul considered himself to be rightful heir to the manuscript.

The sea was freezing and the abject beach strewn in seaweed. We gathered some leathery leaves and drove to the Maitland cemetery on an impulse to cover her gravestone in Atlantic kelp in the mist between acres of graves and angels.

When we got back to the flat, Paul wanted to go out into town. I did not want him to go. "Where's your housemate?"

"Don't worry about him. He stays with his girlfriend most of the time. By the way, the toilet is blocked, so piss in the basin," Paul shouted as he drove to Long Street.

Marley tiles lay lifted off the bathroom floor like discarded cards. There was a gangrenous facecloth and some pubic hairs in the basin. I gave up on bathing and lay down on the three-quarter bed we were meant to share. A cable-knit blanket was pulled over the mattress. No sheets. No curtains on the big sash window. There was a wardrobe, but his clothes were on the floor next to Oupa Boetie's suitcase, flipped open, full of notebooks. The old Olivetti stood on a trestle table amidst piles of books. Some sentences in his handwriting on paper stuck to the wall.

Here I look to be lauded and applauded for nothing said, nothing done. A dreamy conductor of silent symphonies. Haunting notes of fraudulence ring hollow.

A letter for the girl Dudu from Kenya.

You drew me from the closing trench, unearthed me from an inverted grave where I lay buried by rain. Exhumed me by a cycle of thorns and roses: for a garlanded pageant through a town thronged in daylight under an open sky. From which I withheld secret, dark kilometres but not the burgeoning spiral of our incorruptible joy.

There was a photograph stuck next to the letter. A girl with long, curly, dark hair. An intense gaze. Apparently she had grown up on Lake Naivasha in the Rift Valley where cypresses grow like redwoods in the rich soil and bougainvillea twines lakewards like fiery runner beans.

I took a spare sheet from my suitcase and wedged it into the top

188

of the window. Pa always liked to have the curtains drawn against the eyes of the night. I cleaned Paul's room, packed his clothes away and phoned home. He has a room. A job. He pays his own way. The house is clean.

Paul lurched in late and passed out next to me. He stank of smoke and the liquorice sweat of alcohol and something else. Something I did not recognise. He lay snoring and I lay awake. I felt a spreading damp welling from the mattress below me. I jumped up. "Paul you've peed on me!" He stumbled up apologetically. "Shit, I'm sorry." We turned the mattress over and he passed out again. I woke up to cold tea and a letter. *Every night new opportunities for dissipation. Every day the subtle agonies of remorse.*

I dragged the mattress down the stairs into the garden and hosed it down. The housemate came to fetch some clothes and took a Polaroid picture of me. Greg. He wrote campaigns for advertising companies. Can't be staying here, he told me. Paul's coke-fuelled ranting is too distracting. Last month's payday adventure was Paul taking five bergies to the Mount Nelson for dinner, insisting on a wine steward. Greg left a spare key for me. I watched him loping down the road. Too tall and too thin. Somehow lacking the requisite muscle that gave heft to his gender. Greg told me that Paul always wanted to go to Wolwefontein when things got really bad. Once they even got as far as Beaufort West, but the car broke down and they hitched back. That was before Greg went clean.

I walked to the shop and bought kippers and eggs for dinner. Pa ate that for breakfast on holiday as a special treat. Paul came home and stuck a candle into an empty bottle. We drank wine. He hardly spoke and then went to bed. I sat on the balcony and finished a letter to Adi. *The cats and I are missing you.* I drew pictures in the margins of stars and moons and tears falling onto the page. Paul is doing well. Ballpoint pen comets trailing over half-truths. My pen lay limp on the page. It was hard for me to write, not like Paul, whose words and thoughts came like eager whores.

Paul stayed out late almost every night. I moved into Greg's room and paid his portion of the rent. Just until Paul found another house-mate, I promised Ma on the telephone. I registered at the university on the hill. I got my first job as a waitress at an Italian restaurant down the road, where the proprietor treated his white and black staff with equal contempt. He reserved his affection for choleric koi that swam up and down in a large glass tank under his cash register. He spoke to the fish in Italian.

On weekends I worked the lunch shift. Afterwards I went home to clean the cat litter. Greg had been leaving notes. The lease was still in his name and he was not happy with the responsibility. His mounting list of complaints now included Trompie and Saartjie. The unspoken grievance was Greg's girlfriend being solicited away into Paul's bed. His letters were stacking up like an eviction foretold.

I told Paul about his latest message. "Greg is probably just having his period," Paul said going up to the mirror and pulling up his shirt sleeve. He had had *MOM* tattooed on his arm. Upper case black lines with little pin pricks still swollen. He ran water into the basin to shave and looked in the mirror again, "God I am good looking." He winked at me.

Women came and went. He spoke about Dudu feverishly and wrote her long letters that went unanswered. He started writing to scientists at Cambridge, questioning the premise of fractal theory. I found the letters, lying on the sitting room floor at the tail end of long evenings, tapering to an illegible scrawl. *Professor Hawking, if I may be so bold—*

Occasionally Paul spent the weekend sober, making furniture for the house. Beautiful chairs and tables. He spent hours in the backyard with a lathe and measuring tape. On carpentry weekends, he spent the evenings finishing off some writing that he sent to his English teacher from high school. The response was not encouraging. *Pretentious and self-conscious and full of cheap experiences. You can do better.*

There was a man next door who greeted me every day from his balcony. He was on a sports' scholarship at the university and believed in God and "ken jou vyand", know your enemy. I bought a bicycle. He helped me with the falling chain. I fell into his arms. I put a knife into Adi. When I finally ended our relationship of many years over the telephone across the ocean, he said he wanted me to be happy because he loved me. Nadia cried on the phone. Ma told me I was like Paul.

Paul thought my remorse was funny. "Don't bring that hillbilly into my house, though. One must maintain standards," he said. The man next door with the clean shirts and the hard body did not read. After a few weeks I took him across the windy parade to the town hall, past whipped palms draped in plastic bags, and we listened to the symphony orchestra bleating its dues during rehearsal. I told him it was over. He said he now knew what it was like to be used for his body. I said I was sorry. We went back to his house and back to his bed.

I sat on the steps and cleaned Saartjie's eyes with cotton wool dipped in hot water. Cats' eyes grow mangy in the unremitting summer wind. When the wind was not unrelenting, the heat was. The hills beyond Blouberg took on the look of smouldering ash, aridly dwindling into Namib desert in the far north.

A whore came to the front gate and asked if she could use the toilet. Paul had let her in before. She came upstairs and I followed her into Paul's room when she started throwing his clothes out the window. "What are you doing?" I yelled. "He owes me money." Below the window in the street her pimp was catching safari suits and second-hand shoes Paul bought from the Salvation Army in Long Street. She tried to throw out the freemason suitcase Paul had stolen from Oupa but had never opened out of superstition.

"What does he owe you?!" I shouted as I grabbed the suitcase. She let go and smiled at me. Then she stomped down the stairs and was gone.

I stood on the balcony and watched her leave with the pimp and the stolen clothes. A silver Rolls Royce parked further down the road and Paul climbed out of the passenger seat. The stately car glided slowly back into the traffic and disappeared. Paul opened the gate and ran up the steps towards me. "That was your ex father-in-law. He phoned the house hoping to find you. He took me out to lunch in Stellenbosch instead. He has taken the precaution of procuring some valuable real estate in advanced and picturesque decay."

I was relieved not to see Adi's father. Shame clung to me like a needy child. "A prostitute came here and threw your clothes out of the window."

Paul jumped up. "That fucking thieving bitch. She gave me a blowjob on credit. Does she not grasp the concept of lay-by? He ran into his room. "Where's that shirt Christiaan gave me?" He leaned out the window and swore at the whores under the traffic light.

I went back to the balcony and sat down. "I can't believe you slept with a prostitute."

"I did not fuck her. Sucking me off was her idea. I felt kind of horny anyway so I was open to persuasion, but out of pocket." He jumped up again and screamed at the pimp driving past, "You fucking thieving cunt!" Then he sat down and laughed and lit up a cigarette.

"We went book shopping after lunch, your ex father-in-law and I, in that little university town with white walls. I asked a sweet old lady at the second-hand bookshop if there was nothing in there with any intellectual content. Do you know what she said?"

"What?"

"That sort of thing is not very popular round here, my dear."

He blew out a smoke ring. "He asked me where the beautiful Dominique was, so I told him you were having your brains fucked out."

I stood up and dropped Saartjie. She went mewling back inside.

"I cannot believe you said that. I fucking can't believe you."

"What are you getting so upset about?"

I ran inside and lay on the bed weeping. I cried and cried. I felt bad. I was bad.

Eventually Paul stood in the doorway. "Cheer up," he said. He sat down on the bed with a tray on his knees. He took out a small white folded triangle from his pocket and unwrapped it.

"I've been paid for that article I wrote for *Loslyf*. The only moral thing to do with the proceeds of pornography is to buy drugs."

He decanted the white powder into long lines on a tray. And one very short line.

"Have some. It's like having a hard-on in your head."

"But what if I die?" I thought about Ma.

He took a bottle of tequila from his cupboard.

"The small line. You won't die."

I woke up to a quiet house with my legs stuck to the fake leather sofa. Another night into which memory had disappeared without leaving any imprint. Paul was still sitting on the small balcony, staring out at the sea and smoking. Dudu had sent a letter saying it would never work. I was leaving for the farm on the Greyhound bus. The university was closed for the holidays.

Paul took me to the station. In my luggage was the violin he gave me by way of apology for the stolen guitar. He bought it with what he called his emigration savings. There was work in England for carpenters. He said he needed to get away from here. Away from the drugs.

The engine drew the bus out of the wind into endless dry kilometres that lay beyond a toothed pass.

CHAPTER 14

The call came deep in the night. Pa was away making good on his dream to stand on the roof of Africa. Occluded by ice. At the foot of the mountain a porter waited with a note. Nadia and Boetie slept while Ma steadied herself against her desk, alabaster and tall in her nightie like a young girl. Christiaan folded open Ma's address book.

"It's not true," I whispered. "It's not true."

Christiaan made the first call to Oupa and Ouma. His words were apostate to mine in the dark dry September night. No lightning. No rain. Clarion lines.

Ma wanted to burn him. "I will go to England and fetch his ashes." I walked up to Ma and took her by the shoulders. "No. You will not burn him. You will bring him home."

Time flies and time stands still. We pass through time. She is not swayed by us. The vlei spills into the pan. A moorhen glides. Willows drop braids into water. Buried flowers in the darkened garden strain against the soil.

By sunrise all the women from the stat were sweeping and cleaning around the house. They had come unbidden. Ma stood by the window watching them. Martha edged her upstairs to change.

The protocol of solace marked the hours.

Food was brought. Flowers were sent. People came from all over. Family. Neighbours. Those from town who had not come to our house for many years. The dominee. The priest. The police. Ishmael Mabitle's brother. Wolwefontein's people. Pa's family from the Southern Free State. Terror Lekota, who had lost his daughter the year before, with his bodyguards. Terror held Ma. Dudu gathered herself across airports of the North to be where Paul no longer was. Eunice bought herself a bus ticket. Stompie Lekgetha walked all the way from the township at eighty-three, crooked with arthritis. She who used to warn us not to climb trees because we would break. We used to laugh at her broken sentences. Paul's old friends who could not take it any more. The other ones. There to stake a claim.

When Pa returned from Mount Kilimanjaro Adi fetched Pa from the airport and drove him to the farm. We waited for them in the driveway. A tracery of green on apricot branches. The flocking of quealeas into cindery hedges. Adi helped Pa into the house. He turned to Adi and said, "Thank you, my son."

They sent Paul's body back in a casket. The closest depot for the dead was in Klerksdorp. A mining town forged from unforgiving seams, by the end of winter a desultory vacant lot of dust and scrap metal. Pa and I drove to the mortuary to identify the body. Dudu came with. Horses huddled behind sagging fences, facing the still-distant sun. On the outskirts of the township were rows upon rows of freshly dug graves. "Look, Pappa, someone has put up crosses." He put his hand on my arm. "Those are frames for road signs still to come." Doves were racing us as pale grey as the midday.

Abel and Mary Dlamini stood outside the mortuary. Abel held a Bible to his chest and Pa went into Mary's arms. That was the only time he cried. The mortician hovered with his pen and documents. Mary was pleased with Dudu. "She would have been a good wife for our Paul."

We were taken inside. Bodies lay on makeshift catafalques. Paul's hair had been combed into a middle parting. Dudu ran out.

"Please do something to his hair," Pa said.

I knelt down. I ruffled my hand through his soft hair. Beautiful and healthy he lay under his death mask. Shoes laced up for walking. I undid the buttons on his shirt. There was stitching where they had cut him open. I lay my head on his silent chest. I kissed his cold cheekbones. I stroked his eyelids. Underneath, irises once bloomed in the water of life.

"Come, we must go," Pa said.

"No, Pa. We're taking him home."

I spoke to the undertaker. After the soft organs are taken out, a body is sewn closed and embalmed. The rot is removed. The smell of decay deferred. "Perhaps," he suggested softly, "it would be better if we brought him in the hearse tomorrow. It's already been paid for."

"We will take him now, thank you."

The mortician nodded heavily amidst the piped dirges and drapery. They gave us his satchel marked *Paul Michiel Botha the 6th*. Inside was a spoon, elastic bands and a pocket Gideon Bible bound in green leather. Also some pencils, a paint chart and a syringe. We carried him to the Landrover in his pine coffin. The cheapest one on offer. That's what Ma wanted. To be frugal. To be exemplary. To show the farm staff: don't waste money on the dead.

Dudu and I locked arms to keep the coffin in place. The nylon rope handles chafed. At the farm gate, Pa got out, took off his cap and stared down at the vlei. The initiation hut of last winter was mouldering into its woven grass foundations. Women were forbidden to go there.

Pa walked round to where Dudu was sitting and cleared his throat. "Paul wrote to me about this wonderful young woman for whom he wanted to change his life. I want you to know how grateful I am that he could end his life on such a high note of hope." He put his cap back on, got into the driver's seat and cursed the starter engine for failing.

At the house they waited for us. Vygie, Selina, Martha, Mad Magdaleen, Eunice. Oupa with the wild birds on his shoulder. Nadia like a frightened foal in a forest of lost adults. Christiaan, Cardow, Adi and Fritz carried the coffin into the sitting room reserved for special occasions. They laid him out on the brass-buttoned coffee table that Oupa Bob made for Ma's birthday years ago. Eunice was angry about the coffin. She said Paul deserved better. When the lid was lifted, the women wailed. Boetie and Firi were playing outside. They stopped. They started again. Christiaan fetched whiskey. No one drank. Ma whispered to me, "I am not going to cry at the funeral tomorrow because I want Paul to be proud of me."

Outside small cloud shoals were forming. The season was turning.

you went into the earth on lowering ropes
a lamed angel in the time of bloodwood
and flowering stones
you were gone

softly folded like linen into a press
like ash into soil

your brother scraped the road at daybreak
his heart spilt blood
on the long sleeves of his best shirt
a young person's funeral is always big
like pa said
do you still remember?
there were worn arum lilies
starched tablecloths
lime water for mourners
tapped from the sump
fished clean of drowned bats
they who inflect the twilight
on wolwefontein

truths were spoken
about your wry smile
under the shadow tree of knowledge

I swept crushed petals from your grave
lay a cushion against the clods
under ouma's blanket smelling of naphthalene
I wanted to sleep there
the girl in your letters
held my hand
(fingers like strings over a violin bridge
for the song of the snowbird
as you composed her
on loose pages
in the surrendered estate
of your suicide)

she spoke singsong english
like eileen from aandson way back
with your stamp collection as parting gift
do you still remember?
then rain came as closing prayer
out of the turning season
I went without proof or keepsake
into a dank descent of night

soil must subside
we may not

after a year a man from kroonstad
brought a block of granite
on the appointed day
grass was cut
hinges oiled
the hallway clock stopped
the dairy herd sold
pa builds roads without direction
christiaan locks his door
ouma sits at a window
in a nursing home next to the sea
she says she is going upriver tomorrow
there is not enough room on the boat

along a windswept peninsula
behind towers whiter than fresh chalk
is a witch with a soul inventory
a man with a chisel
flayed me
gutted like a live fish
the witch shook my scarred arms
her eyes wide and auguring
like a deer in a book

she said let him go
(I looked for you in the wrong places)

here is a map

follow the late afternoon water birds over schoemansdrif
sometimes there are wreaths against pylons
if you came now
a pretty purple weed is treading south
paling in poor soil
there is bellsong in ditches
poplars silvering wells
scrap implements rusting
in paper flowers of blue thistle

past vredefort a peach orchard mantles
the bend in the road and soft deceptive thorns
defend the prickly pear
beyond the oak avenues of makvoël
between blades of hocked grass
is a mule
a dry palm
a grey saltpan
with a brocade of flamingos as relief
songlines scored in doves

at dusk the evening star
will draw mercury into her ambit
as beacon fire for you

turn left on pa's new road
cambered against the rain
the mourning dove will guide you
with ash-covered wings
through the impending flame cloud

you will see
sani is building a brick house
there are peacocks in his chicken pen
a code ten on his driver's licence
he came proudly to the back door
to show pa

I am calling you

bird choirs rain psalms
down onto the vagabond lawns

the night beats against the walls of hindsight

ma wears a silk skirt with a neat hem
in the flooded corridors
of my recurring dreams
eau-de-nil cupboards are full of your favourite sweets
paint peels and bleeds to the floor and then up the walls
staining the folds of ma's imaginary dress
she stumbles there
the stuttering gait of the living dead
(so pretty with her narrow waist)
spider webs take deep breaths
dust dances a stately dance
in the absence of weighting
cardow waits hat in hand at the kraal
he mourns the sold herd
just like chopi and willem and petrus

they all died
with pension in sight
now pa does not want to let anyone go
to think they worked their whole lives
for this bit of rest

and that too is denied them
his face darkens
then he says oh well

harvests come and go

a maker plants gooseberries and chinese lanterns
in the firmament night garden
that rots and blooms

a flaming wind sugars your words away

I am calling you

I am waiting under the pepper tree
I will know your voice
don't lose your footing
I have watched the stars burning their footpaths
through the velvet night of memory
heavens kneel and sway
over the chanting grass
longing dries like hooked meat
in buried cellars cracking
as the earth turns

somewhere inside are my children you will never know

I wanted so much
to bind you with words
to our place of origin
to begin again
with a sentry against fate
on a different road
along a pencil stripe
tapering over blue hills

in my yellowing notebook

time rolls and dawdles
like a coin thrown
onto the horizon of the nearing dawn

you always walked ahead